Workbook

Delivering the 2010 GCSE Specification

NEW GCSE MATHS
Edexcel Linear

Matches the 2010 GCSE Specification

· Chris Pearce ·

CONTENTS

INTRODUCTION

Welcome to Collins New GCSE Maths for Edexcel Linear Workbook 1.

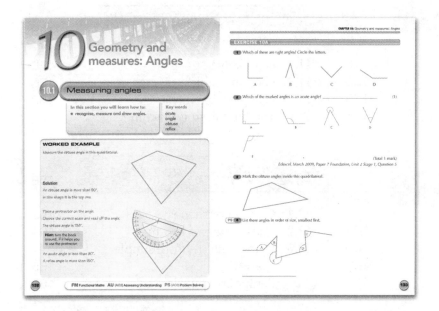

Worked examples

Understand the topic by reading the examples in blue boxes. These take you through questions step by step.

Colour-coded questions

Make progress as you move from red to orange to yellow questions.

Exam practice

Prepare for your exams with past exam questions.

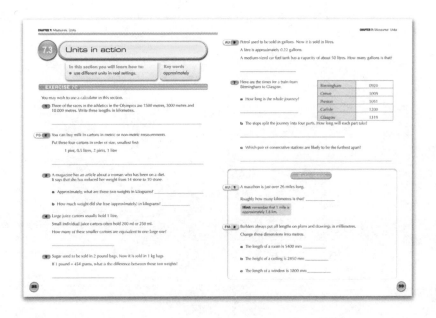

Apply your maths

Practise maths questions in a range of situations in the separate section in yellow at the end of each chapter.

New Assessment Objectives

Check how well you have understood each topic with questions that assess your understanding marked **AU** and questions that test if you can solve problems marked **PS** .

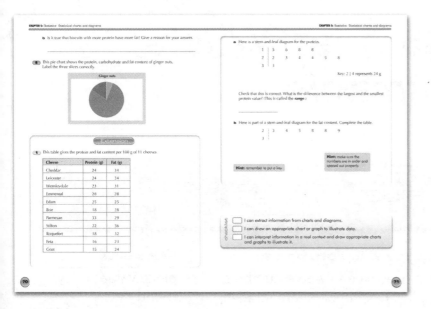

Checklist

Tick off the topics you can do on the checklist at the end of each chapter.

Helpful hints

Use hint boxes to give you tips as you work through the questions.

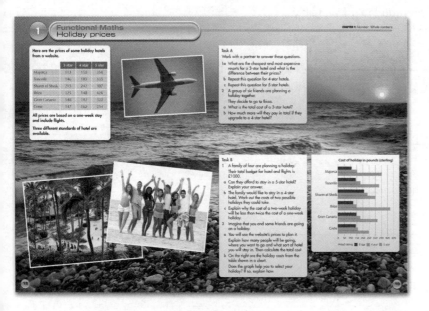

Functional maths

Practise functional maths skills to see how people use maths in everyday life. Look out for practice questions marked **FM** and there are also extra functional maths and problem-solving activities at the end of every chapter.

Answers

Check your own work with the answers at the back of the book.

Glossary

Look up unfamiliar words in the glossary at the back.

1 Number: Whole numbers

1.1 Place value

In this section you will learn how to:
- understand place value in whole numbers
- approximate and round whole numbers in different ways.

Key words
place value
round

WORKED EXAMPLE

The attendance at a football match is 32 845.

Write this number in words and then round it off sensibly.

Solution

32 845 is thirty-two thousand, ⟶ The 5 is 5 units; the 4 stands for 40; the 8 eight hundred and forty-five. stands for 800; the 32 stands for 32 000.

We could round this number to the nearest thousand or the nearest hundred.

32 845 is 33 000 to the ⟶ 32 845 is between 32 000 and 33 000 nearest thousand. and it is closer to 33 000.

32 845 is 32 800 to the nearest hundred.

EXERCISE 1A

1 Write these numbers in figures.

a Four hundred and eight _____

b Six thousand, five hundred and twenty _____

c Eighteen thousand, nine hundred _____

d Seven thousand and fifty _____

FM Functional Maths **AU** (AO2) Assessing Understanding **PS** (AO3) Problem Solving

2 Write these numbers in words.

a 5210 _____

b 16 800 _____

c 5072 _____

3 What is the value of the digit 7 in these numbers? The first one is done for you.

a 4172   seventy

b 7036 _____

c 2711 _____

4 Arrange these three numbers in order, smallest first.

8521   8496   8519 _____

5 Find the largest and smallest numbers in this list.

2972   2083   3132   3088   2772   3129

Largest is _____   Smallest is _____

6 Here is a set of 4 cards. Each card has a number written on it.

    | 4 | | 9 | | 3 | | 7 |

Jill puts all the cards in a line to make the largest possible number.

a Write down the largest possible number she can make. _____ (1)

Jill puts all the cards in a line to make the smallest possible number.

b Write down the smallest possible number that she can make. _____ (1)

Jill puts all the cards in a line to make an even number.

c Write down an even number that she can make. _____ (1)

(Total 3 marks)

Edexcel, March 2008, Paper 10 Foundation, Question 1

7 Round these numbers to the nearest ten.

a 38 _____   **b** 82 _____   **c** 263 _____

8 Round these numbers to the nearest hundred.

a 428 _____   **b** 3580 _____   **c** 43 087 _____

9 a Write the number **three thousand four hundred and twenty five** in figures.

_____ (1)

b Write down the value of 4 in the number 2840 _____ (1)

c Write the number 279 to the nearest hundred. _____ (1)

(Total 3 marks)

Edexcel, November 2008, Paper 10, Foundation, Question 1

Extension

Hint: one and a half million is written like this 1 500 000

1 Five million is written as 5 000 000. Write these numbers in words.

a 8 000 000 _____

b 17 000 000 _____

c 142 000 000 _____

2 Write these numbers in figures.

a Half a million _____

b Seven and a half million _____

3 Round these numbers to the nearest million.

a 4 815 270 _____   **b** 73 199 987 _____

1.2 Calculations with whole numbers

In this section you will learn how to:
- add, subtract, multiply and divide whole numbers.

Key words

add
difference
divide
multiply
subtract

WORKED EXAMPLE

43 people are travelling to a wedding in large cars.

Each car can take six passengers.

How many cars do they need?

Solution

This problem requires a division: ──────────→ $43 \div 6 = 7$ remainder 1

They need eight cars and there will
be five spare seats. ──────────→ 7 is <u>not</u> the correct answer in this case
because one person would be left behind.

EXERCISE 1B

Do not use a calculator in this exercise.

Hint: you could use a number line or a column method if you want.

1. Do these additions using any method you like.

   Use the middle column for any calculations you want to make.

		Calculations	Answer
a	192 + 23		
b	423 + 98		
c	1477 + 281		

2 Do these subtractions using any method you like.

		Calculations	Answer
a	190 – 27		
b	423 – 198		
c	1477 – 429		

3 Do these multiplications using any method you like.

		Calculations	Answer
a	172 × 6		
b	23 × 9		
c	4 × 325		

4 Do these divisions using any method you like.

		Calculations	Answer
a	56 ÷ 4		
b	276 ÷ 6		
c	342 ÷ 3		

5 Fill in the missing digits to complete these calculations.

a
```
   8 3
[        ] +
─────────
 1 0 0
```

b
```
 1 0 8
[        ] +
─────────
 1 3 1
```

c
```
   4 7
[        ] −
─────────
   3 4
```

d
```
 2 5 0
[        ] −
─────────
 2 0 8
```

Extension

1 Find the difference between 34×7 and 32×9.

Use the space for your working.

Answer _____

2 If $\bigstar \times 7 = 371$ what number does $\bigstar$ represent?

Use the space for your working.

Hint: can you do this by division?

Answer _____

1.3 Order of operations

In this section you will learn how to:

● carry out a sequence of operations in the correct order.

Key words

add
bracket
divide
multiply
operation
subtract

WORKED EXAMPLE

Reem thinks that $3 + 4 \times 5$ is 35 but she is incorrect?

What is the correct answer?

What did Reem do wrong?

Solution

You must do multiplication or division before addition or subtraction.

$3 + 4 \times 5 = 3 + 20 = 23$ ⟶ 4×5 is 20

Reem did the addition first and said $7 \times 5 = 35$.

EXERCISE 1C

1 Work out each of these.

a $3 \times 2 + 5 = $ _____

b $4 \times 4 + 4 = $ _____

c $4 \times 4 \div 2 = $ _____

d $4 \times 4 - 4 = $ _____

e $5 + 3 \times 2 = $ _____

f $4 + 5 \times 5 = $ _____

2 Evaluate the following.

Hint: work the brackets out first.

a $2 \times (3 + 3) = $ _____

b $10 \div (3 + 2) = $ _____

c $(3 + 7) \div 2 = $ _____

d $(3 + 7) \times 5 = $ _____

e $5 \times (2 + 3) = $ _____

f $6 \times (3 - 2) = $ _____

3 Draw lines connecting the expression on the left with the correct number on the right.

a $2 \times 2 + 6$ 1

b $2 + 6 \div 3$ 12

c $5 - 1 \times 4$ 10

d $(3 + 5) \div 4$ 5

e $4 \times (5 - 2)$ 2

f $20 \div (7 - 3)$ 4

AU 4 Are the following statements true or false? If they are true, write T. If they are false, write F and the correct answer.

a $12 + 6 \div 3 = 6$ _____   b $14 - 4 \times 2 = 20$ _____

c $16 \div 2 + 2 = 10$ _____   d $8 - 2 \times 2 = 4$ _____

e $2 + 4 \times 3 = 14$ _____   f $6 \times 2 + 8 = 20$ _____

g $21 - 8 \times 2 = 26$ _____   h $(12 - 3) \times 4 = 36$ _____

i $20 \div (5 + 5) = 9$ _____   j $(40 - 20) \div 10 = 38$ _____

5 Frankie says that $15 - 3 \times 2 = 24$
Frankie is wrong.
Explain why.

_____

_____

_____

(Total 1 mark)

Edexcel, November 2008, Paper 9, Foundation, Question 5

AU 6 Put in three different numbers to make this correct.

____ + ____ × ____ = 17

Extension

1 Work out these.

a $3 \times 3 + 4 \times 4 =$ _____

> **Hint:** work out both of the multiplications first.

b $(12 - 8) - (5 - 3) =$ _____

> **Hint:** work out both of brackets first.

PS 2 How many different answers can you get by putting the numbers 2, 4 and 6 into this expression?

____ + ____ × ____

I can make _____ different answers. They are _____ .

3 Work out these.

a $10 + 20 \div 5 =$ _____   **b** $(10 + 20) \div 5 =$ _____

PS 4 Show how to arrange these four number cards together with the operation signs + and × to make 23.

| 2 | 3 | 4 | 5 |

You may use the operation signs more than once.

You must not use brackets.

You must use all four numbers.

_____

PS 5 Show how to arrange these four number cards together with the operation signs – and × to make 1.

| 6 | 7 | 7 | 8 |

You may use the operation signs more than once.

You must not use brackets.

You must use all four numbers.

_____

1.4 Using whole numbers

In this section you will learn how to:
- choose the appropriate operation in a real-life context
- carry out calculations correctly and interpret the results.

Key words
add
difference
divide
multiply
subtract

EXERCISE 1D

Answer these questions without using a calculator.

1 At a football match between Manchester United and Arsenal, the attendance was 75 095.

   a What does the 9 stand for? _____

   b Write the attendance in words. _____

   _____

   On the same day, Chelsea played Burnley and the attendance was 40 906.

   c What does the 9 stand for in the Chelsea attendance? _____

   d Write the Chelsea attendance to the nearest thousand. _____

2 This table shows the attendance at three football matches one weekend.

Home team	Attendance
Stockport	4680
Exeter City	5333
Oldham	5125

   a Which team had the highest attendance?

   _____

b What was the total attendance for the Stockport and Oldham games?

_____

c What was the difference between the Stockport and Exeter attendances?

_____

3 Rachid has £240 in the bank. He takes out £75. How much does he have left?

_____

FM 4 A coach company has nine coaches, each with 52 seats.

a How many seats is that all together?

_____

b A school is hiring some of the coaches for a school trip. There will be 220 pupils and 15 adults. How many coaches will they need?

_____

5 A lottery syndicate of eight people wins £3400.
If they share the money equally, how much does each one receive?

_____

6 Marwa has a phone contract. She will pay £23 a month for nine months.
How much will she pay all together?

_____

FM 7 Chloe has bought a car recently. Here are some of her expenses.

Road tax	£180
Insurance	£516
Service	£237

a What is the total cost of these three items?

_____

b She decides to pay the insurance with six monthly payments.
How much will she pay each month?

_____

Extension

AU 1 In 2008, these were the estimates of the populations of three neighbouring countries in Asia.

Country	Population in millions
India	1149
Pakistan	173
Bangladesh	147

a Write down the population of Pakistan in figures.

_____

b What is the difference between the population of India and the other two countries combined?

_____

c At that time, the estimate of the population of the UK was 61 million. Chloe said that the population of Bangladesh is more than twice the population of the UK.
Do you agree? Give a reason for your answer.
Work with a partner on this question. Try to agree on the best way to explain your reason.

_____

checklist

☐ I can understand place value in whole numbers.

☐ I can approximate and round whole numbers in different ways.

☐ I can add, subtract, multiply and divide whole numbers.

☐ I can carry out a sequence of operations in the correct order.

☐ I can choose the appropriate operation in a real-life context.

☐ I can carry out calculations correctly and interpret results.

Here are the prices of some holiday hotels from a website.

	3 star	4 star	5 star
Majorca	113	158	358
Tenerife	146	185	335
Sharm el Sheik	215	242	307
Ibiza	125	148	426
Gran Canaria	148	182	322
Crete	147	162	254

All prices are based on a one-week stay and include flights.

Three different standards of hotel are available.

Task A

Work with a partner to answer these questions.

1a What are the cheapest and most expensive resorts for a 3-star hotel and what is the difference between their prices?

 b Repeat this question for 4-star hotels.

 c Repeat this question for 5-star hotels.

2 A group of six friends are planning a holiday together.
  They decide to go to Ibiza.

 a What is the total cost of a 3-star hotel?

 b How much more will they pay in total if they upgrade to a 4-star hotel?

Task B

1 A family of four are planning a holiday.
  Their total budget for hotel and flights is £1000.

 a Can they afford to stay in a 5-star hotel? Explain your answer.

 b The family would like to stay in a 4-star hotel. Work out the costs of two possible holidays they could take.

 c Explain why the cost of a two-week holiday will be less than twice the cost of a one-week holiday.

2 Imagine that you and some friends are going on a holiday.

 a You will use the website's prices to plan it.
  Explain how many people will be going, where you want to go and what sort of hotel you will stay in. Then calculate the total cost.

 b On the right are the holiday costs from the table shown in a chart.
  Does the graph help you to select your holiday? If so, explain how.

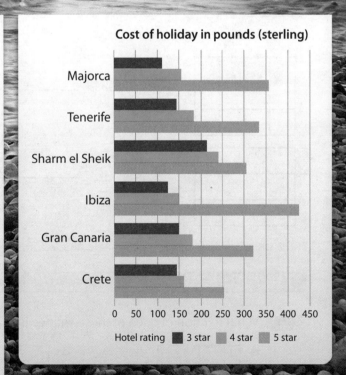

Cost of holiday in pounds (sterling)

Hotel rating ■ 3 star ■ 4 star ■ 5 star

2 Number: Fractions

Recognising fractions

In this section you will learn how to:
- describe fractions in diagrams
- recognise equivalent fractions.

Key words
equivalent
fraction
multiple

WORKED EXAMPLE

Show that $\frac{4}{12}$ and $\frac{1}{3}$ are equivalent fractions.

Solution

We can draw diagrams to show this.

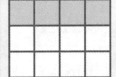

$\frac{4}{12}$ is shaded ⟶ There are 12 equal sections and 4 are shaded.

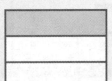

$\frac{1}{3}$ is shaded ⟶ There are 3 equal sections and 1 is shaded.

The same amount of each diagram is shaded. This shows that $\frac{4}{12}$ and $\frac{1}{3}$ are equivalent.

EXERCISE 2A

1 What fraction of each of these shapes is shaded?

a

b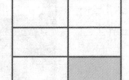

c

FM Functional Maths **AU** (AO2) Assessing Understanding **PS** (AO3) Problem Solving

2 Shade in the fraction indicated underneath each shape.

a

$\dfrac{3}{4}$

b

$\dfrac{1}{4}$

c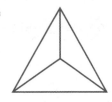

$\dfrac{2}{3}$

d

$\dfrac{1}{6}$

3 What equivalent fractions do these diagrams show?

a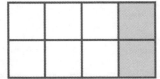

_____ and _____ are equivalent.

b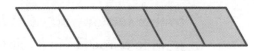

_____ and _____ are equivalent.

AU 4 Put a circle round the fraction shaded. Give a reason for your answer.

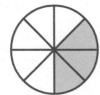

$\dfrac{1}{3}$ $\dfrac{3}{5}$ $\dfrac{3}{8}$ $\dfrac{5}{8}$

Reason: _____

AU 5 What fraction is shaded here? Write your answer as three different equivalent fractions.

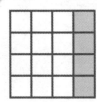

_____ or _____ or _____

Extension

AU 1 Draw diagrams to show that $\frac{3}{4}$ and $\frac{5}{8}$ are <u>not</u> equivalent.

2.2 Using equivalent fractions

In this section you will learn how to:
- write a fraction in its simplest form
- understand how to find and use equivalent fractions.

Key words

cancel
denominator
equivalent
fraction
multiple

WORKED EXAMPLE

Which is larger, $\frac{3}{4}$ or $\frac{2}{3}$?

<u>Solution</u>

One way to answer this is to start by listing equivalent fractions:

$\frac{3}{4} = \frac{6}{8} = \frac{9}{12} = \frac{12}{16} = \ldots$ ⟶ Can you see the multiples of 3 and the multiples of 4?

$\frac{2}{3} = \frac{4}{6} = \frac{6}{9} = \frac{8}{12} = \ldots$ ⟶ What multiples can you see this time?

Find two fractions in the lists with the same bottom number (denominator).

$\frac{3}{4} = \frac{9}{12}$ and $\frac{2}{3} = \frac{8}{12}$. ⟶ The bottom number is 12.

Now $\frac{9}{12}$ is bigger than $\frac{8}{12}$, ⟶ The difference between them is $\frac{1}{12}$.
so this shows that $\frac{3}{4}$ is larger than $\frac{2}{3}$.

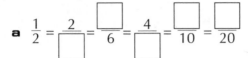

EXERCISE 2B

1 Complete each of these statements.

a $\dfrac{1}{2} = \dfrac{2}{\Box} = \dfrac{\Box}{6} = \dfrac{4}{\Box} = \dfrac{\Box}{10} = \dfrac{\Box}{20}$

b $\dfrac{3}{5} = \dfrac{6}{\Box} = \dfrac{9}{\Box} = \dfrac{\Box}{20} = \dfrac{\Box}{25} = \dfrac{30}{\Box}$

> Be careful with the last ones – draw a fraction diagram if it helps.

2 Complete this list of fractions equivalent to $\frac{2}{3}$.

$$\dfrac{2}{3} = \dfrac{4}{\Box} = \dfrac{6}{\Box} = \dfrac{8}{\Box} = \dfrac{10}{\Box} = \dfrac{\Box}{\Box}$$

3 Write down four fractions equivalent to $\frac{3}{5}$.

_____   _____   _____   _____

4 Find the missing number in each case.

$\dfrac{1}{4} = \dfrac{\Box}{20}$ $\dfrac{1}{8} = \dfrac{\Box}{32}$ $\dfrac{2}{5} = \dfrac{\Box}{15}$

5 Cancel down each of the following fractions.

> **Hint:** what number can both the top and bottom numbers be divided by?

a $\dfrac{6}{20} =$ _____   **b** $\dfrac{20}{30} =$ _____

c $\dfrac{16}{20} =$ _____   **d** $\dfrac{16}{64} =$ _____

6 Arrange these fractions in order of size.

Start with the smallest fraction.

$$\dfrac{2}{3} \qquad \dfrac{1}{2} \qquad \dfrac{1}{4} \qquad \dfrac{2}{5}$$

_____

(Total 2 marks)

Edexcel, March 2008, Paper 10 Foundation, Question 11

AU 7 Put these fractions in order from smallest to largest.

$$\frac{1}{2} \quad \frac{1}{3} \quad \frac{4}{6}$$

_____

Explain how you decided. _____

_____

8 Use equivalent fractions to add fractions together. The first one is done for you.

a $\frac{1}{2} + \frac{1}{8} = \frac{4}{8} + \frac{1}{8} = \frac{5}{8}$ **b** $\frac{1}{4} + \frac{3}{8} = $ _____ $+$ _____ $= $ _____

c $\frac{1}{3} + \frac{1}{2} = $ _____ $+$ _____ $= $ _____   **d** $\frac{2}{3} + \frac{1}{4} = $ _____ $+$ _____ $= $ _____

e $\frac{1}{2} + \frac{1}{10} = $ _____ $+$ _____ $= $ _____ $= $ _____

Extension

1 Explain why $\frac{1}{2} + \frac{1}{4} = \frac{3}{4}$.

Reason: _____

2 Look at this example.

$$\frac{5}{8} + \frac{1}{2} = \frac{5}{8} + \frac{4}{8} = \frac{9}{8}$$ $\frac{8}{8} = 1.$ $\frac{9}{8}$ is more than 1. We write $\frac{9}{8} = 1\frac{1}{8}$.

Do these the same way.

a $\frac{3}{4} + \frac{1}{2} = $

b $\frac{7}{10} + \frac{1}{2} = $

c $\frac{1}{2} + \frac{2}{3} = $

3 Subtraction uses equivalent fractions too.

$$\frac{5}{8} - \frac{1}{4} = \frac{5}{8} - \frac{2}{8} = \frac{3}{8}$$

Hint: make the bottom numbers the same.

Try these.

a $\frac{3}{4} - \frac{1}{2}$ = _____ = _____

b $\frac{7}{10} - \frac{1}{2}$ = _____ = _____ = _____

c $\frac{2}{3} - \frac{1}{4}$ = _____ = _____

2.3 Calculating fractions

In this section you will learn how to:
- calculate fractions of money, quantities or measurements.

Key words
fraction

WORKED EXAMPLE

In a sale, the price of a dress is reduced by $\frac{2}{3}$. It originally cost £85.95. How much will you save?

<u>Solution</u>

Divide by 3 to find $\frac{1}{3}$.

85.95 ÷ 3 = 28.65 —————————→ Use a calculator.

Multiply by 2 to find $\frac{2}{3}$.

28.65 × 2 = 57.3

You will save £57.30. —————————→ Do not forget that 0 at the end for money.

EXERCISE 2C

1 Find these fractions of 100p.

a $\frac{1}{2}$ of 100p = _____   **b** $\frac{3}{4}$ of 100p = _____

c $\frac{3}{5}$ of 100p = _____   **d** $\frac{3}{10}$ of 100p = _____

e Use your answers to put the fractions $\frac{1}{2}$, $\frac{3}{4}$, $\frac{3}{5}$, $\frac{3}{10}$ in order, smallest first.

_____

2 Find each of these.

a $\frac{1}{3}$ of 24 = _____   **b** $\frac{1}{4}$ of 24 = _____

c $\frac{1}{8}$ of 24 = _____   **d** $\frac{1}{5}$ of 30 = _____

e $\frac{1}{2}$ of 30 = _____   **f** $\frac{1}{10}$ of 30 = _____

3 Calculate each of these quantities.

a $\frac{2}{3}$ of 24 kg = _____   **b** $\frac{3}{4}$ of 24 g = _____

c $\frac{4}{5}$ of £30 = _____   **d** $\frac{7}{10}$ of 30 m = _____

Remember: show all your workings and don't forget the units in your answers.

AU 4 Which would you rather have: $\frac{2}{3}$ of £240 or $\frac{3}{8}$ of £400? Give a reason for your answer.

Answer: _____

Reason: _____

5 **a** Work out $\frac{1}{5}$ of 30 _____ (1)

    b Work out $\frac{3}{4}$ of 20 _____ (2)

(Total 3 marks)

Edexcel, May 2008, Paper 12 Foundation, Question 8

6 A special offer on a packet says: 500 g + $\frac{1}{5}$ extra free!

    a What is the weight that is given for free? _____

    b What is the total weight of the special offer packet? _____

7 A box contains 200 tissues. Toby takes $\frac{3}{5}$ of these tissues.
Work out how many tissues he takes.

_____

(Total 2 marks)

Edexcel, June 2008, Foundation, Question 5

Extension

PS **1** Kofi wants to buy a new pair of shoes. He has £15, which is $\frac{1}{3}$ of what he needs.

How much are the shoes?

_____

2.4 Using fractions

In this section you will learn how to:
- use fractions in everyday contexts
- explain ideas using mathematical language
- complete calculations accurately.

Key words
equivalent
fraction

EXERCISE 2D

1 Here is a picture with a wide frame.

What fraction is the painting of the whole thing?

Circle the closest answer from these.

$\frac{1}{2}$ $\frac{3}{4}$ $\frac{1}{5}$ $\frac{5}{8}$

Give a reason for your answer.

_____

2 This window has eight small panes.

$\frac{3}{4}$ of them are broken.

Show one way this could be the case.

AU 3 You can see windows like this in old houses.

The panes are diamonds and triangles.

Explain how you know that <u>half</u> the window is made up of diamond-shaped panes.

Reason: _____

_____

4 Bricks in a wall can be:

stretchers Two headers are the same length as one stretcher:

or headers.

a What fraction of this wall is headers? What fraction is stretchers?

Write your answers in the simplest possible form.

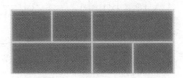

Headers _____

Stretchers _____

b Answer the same questions for this wall.

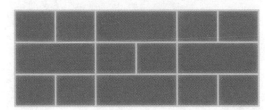

Headers _____

Stretchers _____

PS 5 The distance from Bristol to Coventry is 120 miles.

Usain has driven half way. Ceri has driven $\frac{3}{4}$ of the way. Barak has driven $\frac{2}{5}$ of the way.

Their positions are shown on this line.

Bristol ├──────────────×───×──────────×──────────┤ Coventry

Put names on the crosses.

Write in the distances between them.

> **Hint:** start by finding each fraction of 120 miles.

Extension

1 Jed is 12 years old. His mother is 36 years old. His sister Ami is 16 years old.

Fill in the missing fractions.

Hint: simplify $\frac{12}{36}$.

Jed is _____ of his mother's age.   Jed is _____ of Ami's age.

2 Here are the populations of four countries, in millions.

a Fill in the missing fraction:

The population of Greece is _____ of the population of Spain.

Country	Millions
Great Britain	60
Spain	40
Greece	10
Germany	8

b Write two more sentences using fractions to compare the populations of countries.

_____

_____

FM 3 Look at these three offers.

Which one is the best value? Give a reason for your answer.

- Sale price $\frac{3}{4}$ of marked price
- Prices reduced by $\frac{2}{3}$
- Everything is half price

_____

_____

_____

_____

Hint: you could choose a starting price and see what the effect of each offer is.

checklist

☐ I can describe fractions in diagrams.

☐ I can recognise equivalent fractions.

☐ I can write a fraction in its simplest form.

☐ I can understand how to find and use equivalent fractions.

☐ I can calculate fractions of money, quantities or measurements.

☐ I can use fractions in everyday contexts.

☐ I can explain ideas using mathematical language.

☐ I can complete calculations accurately.

You can see lots of fractions on a clock face.

These clock faces show:

$\frac{1}{12}$ $\frac{1}{6}$ (or $\frac{2}{12}$) $\frac{1}{4}$ (or $\frac{3}{12}$) $\frac{1}{3}$ (or $\frac{4}{12}$) $\frac{5}{12}$ $\frac{1}{2}$ (or $\frac{6}{12}$)

Task A

We can use clock faces to add fractions.

Example: what is $\frac{1}{3} + \frac{1}{4}$?

You can see that $\frac{1}{3} + \frac{1}{4} = \frac{7}{12}$.

Count the 12ths round from the top.

Use a clock face to find the following fractions.
Simplify your answer if you can.

a $\frac{1}{2} + \frac{1}{4}$ b $\frac{1}{2} + \frac{1}{12}$ c $\frac{1}{12} + \frac{1}{4}$ d $\frac{1}{3} + \frac{1}{12}$

e $\frac{1}{3} + \frac{1}{6}$ f $\frac{1}{6} + \frac{1}{12}$ g $\frac{1}{3} + \frac{1}{2}$ h $\frac{1}{2} + \frac{1}{3} + \frac{1}{6}$

Hint: a unit fraction means that the denominator is a positive integer and the numerator is 1, for example: $\frac{1}{4}$ or $\frac{1}{2}$.

Task B

The Ancient Egyptians wrote fractions in a strange way.

They only had symbols for **unit fractions**.

All other fractions had to be written as a **sum** of **different** unit fractions.

They would write $\frac{3}{4}$ as $\frac{1}{2} + \frac{1}{4}$.

They would not write it as $\frac{1}{4} + \frac{1}{4} + \frac{1}{4}$ because the unit fractions had to be different.

Your clock face arithmetic has shown how the Egyptians wrote some fractions.

Look back at your answers to see how they wrote the following.

1a $\frac{5}{12}$ b $\frac{5}{6}$ c $\frac{7}{12}$

2 Investigate to find what other fractions you can write in the Egyptian way.

Use a calculator to do the additions. Make sure it has a fraction button! Work with a partner and share your results.

You could make a poster to display what you find.

Interesting fact

No one knows **why** the Ancient Egyptians wrote fractions in such a strange way. Why do you think they did?

3 Number: Negative numbers

3.1 Understanding negative numbers

In this section you will learn how to:
- put negative numbers in order
- use negative numbers in different contexts.

Key words
difference
negative number
temperature

WORKED EXAMPLE

Is −8°C hotter or colder than 5°C? What is the difference between these two temperatures?

Solution

Draw a number line to help you.

−8   0   5

We can see that −8°C is colder. ⟶ It is further to the left.

There are 13 degrees between them. ⟶ 8 degrees from −8 to 0 and then another 5.
8 + 5 = 13

The difference is 13 degrees. ⟶ We could write −8 + 13 = 5 or we could write
5 − −8 = 13.

EXERCISE 3A

1 This thermometer shows temperatures in °C.

Mark these temperatures on the thermometer:

5°C   18°C   −5°C   −12°C

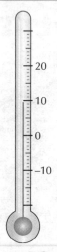

20

10

0

−10

FM Functional Maths   **AU** (AO2) Assessing Understanding   **PS** (AO3) Problem Solving

2 Label each arrow with the correct temperature. Choose from these.

25°C   −25°C   40°C   −60°C   75°C   −75°C

> **Hint:** two of the numbers will not be used.

3 Put these temperatures in order, from coldest to warmest.

12°C,   −15°C,   8°C,   −20°C,   −32°C,   4°C,   −60°C

_____

4 The table shows the temperatures in three cities at noon one day.

City	Temperature
Oslo	−13°C
New York	−5°C
Cape Town	9°C

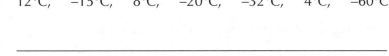

a Work out the difference in the temperature between Oslo and New York.

_____°C   (1)

b Work out the difference in temperature between Cape Town and Oslo.

_____°C   (1)

(Total 2 marks)

Edexcel, June 2008, Paper 2 Foundation, Question 9

5 Here are some temperature changes. For each one, write how many degrees the temperature has risen or fallen. The first one has been done for you.

a From −1°C to 4°C   rise of 5 degrees

b From 7°C to 2°C   _____

c From 3°C to −5°C   _____

d From −5°C to −8°C   _____

e From −6°C to 6°C   _____

6 At 2pm one winter's day, the temperature was 6°C. By midnight it had fallen to –3°C.

How many degrees colder was it at midnight? _____

AU 7 You can use negative numbers to show when you have gone into debt.

For example, if you have £20 in your bank account and spend £30, you are £10 in debt.

You could write your balance as –£10.

Write the results of the following, using negative numbers if you need to.

a Start with £50 and spend £80. Bank balance is _____ .

b Start with –£20 and spend another £15. Bank balance is _____ .

> **Hint:** if you start with a debt, it will get bigger!

c Start with £30, spend £40 and then pay in £15. Bank balance is _____ .

d Start with –£50, spend £10, pay in £40. Bank balance is _____ .

Extension

1 We can write temperature changes to look like a sum.

For example, if a night time temperature of –5°C increases by 8 degrees during the day to 3°C, we can write:
$$-5 + 8 = 3$$
Try to write these in the same way and find the final temperatures.

a The temperature rises from –6°C by 10 degrees. _____ _____

b The temperature rises from –9°C by 4 degrees. _____ _____

2 We can write a fall in temperature using subtraction.

For example, if the temperature falls from –3°C by 5 degrees, we can write:
$$-3 - 5 = -8$$
Write these in the same way and find the final temperatures.

a The temperature falls from 6°C by 8 degrees. _____ _____

b The temperature falls from –9°C by 2 degrees. _____ _____

CHAPTER 3: Number: Negative numbers

3.2 Using negative numbers

In this section you will learn how to:
● use negative numbers in everyday contexts.

Key words
negative number
temperature

EXERCISE 3B

1 One of the coldest places in the USA is Rogers Pass in Montana.

Here are the average monthly minimum temperatures in °C.

Jan	Feb	Mar	Apr	May	Jun	Jul	Aug	Sep	Oct	Nov	Dec
−12.0	−9.2	−5.7	−1.4	3.1	7.1	9.5	8.9	3.9	−0.1	−6.4	−10.3

a Which month is the warmest? _____

b List the four coldest months in order, coldest first. _____

_____

c Describe how the temperature changes through the year. _____

_____

2 The average temperature on Earth is 15°C. The average temperature on the planet Mars is −50°C.

What is the difference between these temperatures? _____

Is Mars hotter or colder than the Earth? Can you think of a reason for this?

_____

37

AU 3 The table shows the temperatures at midnight in 6 cities during one night in 2006.

City	Temperature
Berlin	5°C
London	10°C
Moscow	–3°C
New York	2°C
Oslo	–8°C
Paris	7°C

a Write down the city which had the lowest temperature.

_____°C   (1)

b Work out the difference between London and Moscow.

_____°C   (2)

(Total 3 marks)

Edexcel, June 2008, Paper 10 Foundation, Question 2

PS 4 Ulan Bator in Mongolia has the largest temperature range in the world.

The average January temperature is –32°C. The average July temperature is 54 degrees higher.

Hint: it might help to draw a temperature line.

What is the average July temperature?

_____

AU 5 The gas oxygen is essential for life. It becomes a liquid at –183°C and a solid at –218°C.

a What is the difference between these two temperatures? _____

b Why has no one ever found puddles of liquid oxygen on Earth?

_____

FM 6 Zeeta is keeping her accounts in a spreadsheet. Fill in the missing **balances**.

	Spend	Deposit	Balance
Starting balance	—	—	£20
Shoes	£50	—	−£30
Eating out	£15	—	
Birthday present	—	£20	
Cinema	£6	—	
Reward for good grades	—	£5	
Swimming lesson	£8	—	

Extension

AU 1 Look at Zeeta's spreadsheet in question 6.
Write each line of her accounts as an addition or a subtraction.
The first one is done for you.

Shoes   20 − 50 = −30

Eating out   −30 − 15 = _____

Birthday present   _____ + 20 = _____

Cinema   _____

Reward   _____

Swimming lesson   _____

checklist

☐ I can put negative numbers in order.

☐ I can use negative numbers in different contexts.

☐ I can use negative numbers in everyday contexts.

Average monthly temperatures for July and January

City	July	January	Difference July–January
Accra	25	27	
Beijing	26	–5	
Cairo	28	14	
Cape Town	13	21	
Chennai (Madras)	30	25	
Christchurch	6	17	
Helsinki	17	–6	
Lhasa	16	–2	
Lima	16	22	
London	17	4	
Moscow	19	–10	
Quebec	19	–12	
Reykjavik	11	0	
Sydney	12	22	
Tokyo	25	4	
Vancouver	17	3	
Vladivostok	18	–14	

Reykjavik, Iceland

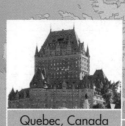
Quebec, Canada

Vancouver, Canada

Lima, Peru

Task A

1 Look at the July temperatures.
   a Write down the two hottest places in July.
   b Write down the two coldest places in July.

2 Look at the January temperatures.
   a Write down the two hottest places in January.
   b Write down the two coldest places in January.

3 Work out the difference between each city's July and January temperatures. Put them in the table.

   Here are two examples.

   Accra temperatures, July – January = 25 – 27 = –2.

   This means that in Accra, July is 2 degrees colder than January.

   Beijing temperatures, July – January = 26 – –5 = 31.

   This means that in Beijing, July is 31 degrees hotter than January.

London, UK

Helsinki, Finland

Moscow, Russia

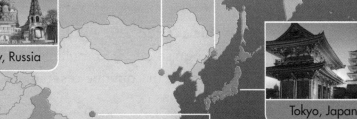
Beijing, China

Vladivostock, Russia

Tokyo, Japan

Cairo, Egypt

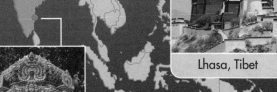
Lhasa, Tibet

Accra, Ghana

Chennai, India

Cape Town,
South Africa

Sydney, Australia

Christchurch,
New Zealand

Task B

1 Look at the differences in the table.

   a Write down the place with the largest temperature difference.

   b Write down the place with the smallest temperature difference.

2 Do you think that the place where you live has a large or small temperature difference between July and January?

   Give a reason for your answer.

4 Number: Properties of numbers

 4.1 **Multiples of whole numbers**

In this section you will learn how to:
- recognise and find multiples of a number
- describe or continue a sequence of numbers.

Key words
multiple
sequence

WORKED EXAMPLE

Find the multiples of 17 between 200 and 250.

Solution

We can find multiples of 17 using a calculator.

$17 \times 10 = 170$ —————————————→ But that is too small.

$17 \times 11 = 187$ —————————————→ And that is too small.

$17 \times 12 = 204$ —————————————→ That is the first one.

$17 \times 13 = 221$ —————————————→ That is another.

$17 \times 14 = 238$ —————————————→ That is another.

$17 \times 15 = 255$ —————————————→ That is too big.

So there are three multiples. They are 204, 221 and 238.

Here is a different method.

Once we have found 204 we can add 17s to find the rest.

$204 + 17 = 221$

$221 + 17 = 238$

$238 + 17 = 255$ —————————————→ And we stop there.

FM Functional Maths **AU** (AO2) Assessing Understanding **PS** (AO3) Problem Solving

EXERCISE 4A

1 Here are some multiples of 5. Write down the next three.

20, 25, 30, 35, 40, _____ , _____ , _____

2 Here are some multiples of 4. Write down the next three.

24, 28, 32, 36, 40, _____ , _____ , _____

3 **a** List the first seven multiples of 8. _____

b List the first seven multiples of 6. _____

c What number is in both lists? _____

4 List the first 6 multiples of 15.

_____

5 List all the multiples of 20 that are less than 150.

_____

6 List the multiples of 3 between 20 and 40.

_____

PS **7** Find a number that is a multiple of 4 **and** a multiple of 5.

_____

AU **8** <u>Two</u> of these numbers are multiples of 5. Circle them.

508   135   264   709   820   92

Give a reason for your answer. _____

AU **9** **a** Here are some multiples of 4. Write down the next three.

120, 124, 128, 132, _____ , _____ , _____

b What can you say about the last digit of any multiple of 4?

_____

c Give a reason why 2083 cannot be a multiple of 4.

_____

Extension

AU **1** We can check whether 785 or 966 are multiples of 23 with a calculator:

$785 \div 23 = 34.1304....$

This is **not** a whole number, so 785 is not a multiple of 23.

$966 \div 23 = 42$

This **is** a whole number, so 966 is a multiple of 23.

Decide whether these statements are true or false. Give a reason each time.

a 741 is a multiple of 39. _____

b 941 is a multiple of 43. _____

c 612 is a multiple of 17. _____

d 988 is a multiple of 26. _____

PS **2** Find a number that is a multiple of 2 and of 3 and of 5. _____

4.2 Factors

In this section you will learn how to:
- find the factors of a number
- identify prime numbers.

Key words

factor
prime number
product

WORKED EXAMPLE

Explain why 847 is not a prime number.

<u>Solution</u>

If 847 is not a prime number, we can find one of its factors.

Let's try.

2 is not a factor of 847. ⟶ 847 is an odd number so 2 is not a factor. No even number can be a factor.

Is 3 a factor? $847 \div 3 = 282.33$ so it is not. ⟶ The answer is not a whole number.

No need to try 4. ⟶ It is an even number.

5 is not a factor. ⟶ 847 does not end in 0 or 5.

Is 7 a factor? $847 \div 7 = 121$, which is a whole number, so **7 is a factor** and that means that 847 is not a prime number.

We could go further and write $847 = 7 \times 121$.

$121 = 11 \times 11$, so $847 = 7 \times 11 \times 11$.

7 and 11 are both prime numbers. A prime number is a whole number with only two factors: itself and 1.

We have written 847 as a product of prime factors.

EXERCISE 4B

1 $15 = 1 \times 15$ $15 = 3 \times 5$

Use these facts to list the four factors of 15.

_____

2 The number 20 has six factors. List them.

_____

AU 3 $13 \times 17 = 221$

    a Use this fact to find two factors of 221. _____

    b Can you find another two? _____

> **Hint:** these are the easy ones we sometimes forget!

AU 4

×	11	23
17	187	391
19	209	437

    a 17 and 11 are factors of 187. Explain how the table shows this.

    _____

    b Use the table to write three more statements about factors.

    _____

    _____

    _____

AU 5 Only one of these statements is correct. Which one?

    A   3 and 6 are factors of 15.   B   17 does not have any factors.

    C   The number 16 has five factors.   D   5 is a factor of 25 and 52.

    Give a reason for your choice.

    Answer: _____ Reason: _____

PS 6 **Prime numbers** only have two factors, 1 and the number itself.

    Examples are 3, 7, 17 and 41.

    List all the prime numbers between 10 and 20.

    _____

AU 7 Here is a list of numbers.

6   13   20   27   34   41

From the list, choose the following. You can use each number more than once.

a two odd numbers _____   **b** two multiples of 3 _____

c a factor of 18 _____   **d** two prime numbers _____

e a factor of 26 _____

Extension

1 **a** Use a calculator to check that $2 \times 3 \times 5 \times 7 = 210$.

b Write down four factors of 210. _____

> **Hint:** use part a. 2 is a factor.

c $2 \times 3 = 6$ and $5 \times 7 = 35$. Show that 6 and 35 are also factors of 210.

_____

PS 2 $1001 = 7 \times 11 \times 13$

a Is 1001 a prime number? _____

b Find as many factors of 1001 as you can.

> **Hint:** there are 8 altogether.

4.3 Square numbers, cube numbers and square roots

In this section you will learn how to:

- understand what square numbers and cube numbers are
- understand the connection between square numbers and square roots
- find a square root using a calculator.

Key words

consecutive
cube number
square number
square root

WORKED EXAMPLE

Find two square numbers that add up to 61.

Solution

You should know the first few square numbers.

They are 1, 4, 9, 16, 25, 36, 49, 64, ... ⟶ That is 1×1, 2×2, 3×3 and so on.

We do not need to go any further. ⟶ We want 2 numbers less than 61.

A bit of trial and improvement shows the answer is 25 and 36 ⟶ To get an odd answer we know we must add an odd number and an even number.

EXERCISE 4C

1 Square numbers can be shown with squares of dots. Here are 16 dots in a square.

Draw squares made up of 9 dots and of 25 dots.

2 The 10th square number is 100, which is 10×10.

a What is the 20th square number? _____

b What is the largest square number that is less than 1000?

Give a reason for your answer.

Answer: _____ Reason: _____

3 We often write square numbers with a small 2 like this: ^{2}

The 4th square number is $4^2 = 4 \times 4 = 16$ (Read 4^2 as 'four squared').

Write down these square numbers.

a $3^2 =$ _____ **b** $7^2 =$ _____ **c** $10^2 =$ _____

4 Find the following.

a $4^2 + 5^2 =$ _____ **b** $6^2 + 7^2 =$ _____

AU 5 Here is a list of numbers.

$$3 \qquad 8 \qquad 11 \qquad 25 \qquad 33 \qquad 41$$

Write down a number from the list which is

a an even number, _____ (1)

b a square number, _____ (1)

c a multiple of 11 _____ (1)

(Total 3 marks)

Edexcel, November 2008, Paper 10 Foundation, Question 2

6 $5^2 = 25$, so the **square root** of 25 is 5. We write $\sqrt{25} = 5$.

Find these square roots. You will need to use a calculator.

a $\sqrt{36} =$ _____ **b** $\sqrt{81} =$ _____ **c** $\sqrt{144} =$ _____

d $\sqrt{225} =$ _____ **e** $\sqrt{900} =$ _____ **f** $\sqrt{1024} =$ _____

> **Interesting fact:** the number 1024 is important in computing and it is often called 1K.

7 Use a calculator to find these square roots. Round them off to two decimal places.

a $\sqrt{91}$ = _____

b $\sqrt{66}$ = _____

c $\sqrt{167}$ = _____

d $\sqrt{1000}$ = _____

8 Check with a calculator that $4 \times 4 \times 4 = 64$. This is called **4 cubed** and it is written as 4^3.

Find these cube numbers.

a 5^3 = _____   **b** 2^3 = _____   **c** 6^3 = _____   **d** 10^3 = _____

PS 9 Find two cube numbers that add up to 91. Give a reason for your answer.

Answer: _____   Reason: _____

10 Here is a list of numbers.

2   4   8   12   16   20   32   40

From the list,

a write down a square number.   _____   (1)

b write down a cube number.   _____   (1)

(Total 2 marks)

Edexcel, March 2008, Paper 9 Foundation, Question 1

> ### Extension

1 We can extend the idea of square and cube numbers.

What do you think that 3^4 means?

_____

Check with a calculator that $3^4 = 81$.

2 Use a calculator to find these.

a $2^4 =$ _____   **b** $5^4 =$ _____

AU **3** Which is larger, 3^4 or 4^3? Give a reason for your answer.

Answer: _____   Reason: _____

PS **4** Write these in order of size, smallest first: 4^2 , 3^3 , 2^4 _____

4.4   # Different types of number

In this section you will learn how to:
- use mathematical terminology consistently and accurately
- use mathematics in meaningful contexts.

Key words
cube number
factor
multiple
prime number
square number
square root

EXERCISE 4D

PS **1** Find two prime numbers which add up to these totals.

a 10 = _____ **b** 16 = _____ **c** 20 = _____

d Find two prime numbers that add up to 40 in as many different ways as you can.

_____

Hint: it will help if you have a list of prime numbers to look at.

AU **2** The 4th square number is 16.

This diagram shows that $16 = 1 + 3 + 5 + 7$.

a This square shows the 5th square number.
Colour it in a similar way.

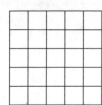

Complete this sentence:

This shows that $25 =$ _____.

You have shown that the first four odd numbers add to 4^2.

You have shown that the first five odd numbers add to 5^2.

b What do you think the first six odd numbers add up to? Check whether you are correct.

_____

AU 3 This time the diagram shows that $16 = 4^2 = 1 + 2 + 3 + 4 + 3 + 2 + 1$.

a Colour this in a similar way.

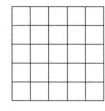

This shows that $25 = 5^2 =$ _____.

b Write a similar statement about 6^2.

_____

FM 4 A celebration dinner is being planned.
There are a lot of rectangular tables which
can seat six people like this.

a Show how people could be seated
round these two tables.

b How many people is that? _____

c Investigate three and more tables in a similar arrangement like this.

Put your results in this table.

Number of tables	1	2	3	4	5
Number of seats	6				

d How does the number of seats increase each time? _____

e How many tables would you need for 30 people? _____

f The tables could be arranged like this instead.

Investigate how many people could be seated with different numbers of tables arranged in this way. You could put your results in a table and describe any patterns you see.

Extension

PS 1 **a** Johanna notices that $1^3 + 2^3 = (1 + 2)^2$.

Check that this is correct. _____

b Johanna wonders if $1^3 + 2^3 + 3^3 = (1 + 2 + 3)^2$.

Check that this is correct. _____

c Complete this in a similar way and check that you are correct.

$1^3 + 2^3 + 3^3 + 4^3 =$ _____

d Can you write another statement like these?

_____

checklist

- [ ] I can recognise and find multiples of a number.
- [ ] I can describe or continue a sequence of numbers.
- [ ] I can find the factors of a number.
- [ ] I can identify prime numbers.
- [ ] I can understand what square numbers and cube numbers are.
- [ ] I can understand the connection between square numbers and square roots.
- [ ] I can find a square root using a calculator.
- [ ] I can use mathematical terminology consistently and accurately.
- [ ] I can use mathematics in meaningful contexts.

Problem Solving
Prime numbers and factors

The prime numbers up to 200 are shaded in this grid.

1	2	3	4	5	6	7	8	9	10
11	12	13	14	15	16	17	18	19	20
21	22	23	24	25	26	27	28	29	30
31	32	33	34	35	36	37	38	39	40
41	42	43	44	45	46	47	48	49	50
51	52	53	54	55	56	57	58	59	60
61	62	63	64	65	66	67	68	69	70
71	72	73	74	75	76	77	78	79	80
81	82	83	84	85	86	87	88	89	90
91	92	93	94	95	96	97	98	99	100
101	102	103	104	105	106	107	108	109	110
111	112	113	114	115	116	117	118	119	120
121	122	123	124	125	126	127	128	129	130
131	132	133	134	135	136	137	138	139	140
141	142	143	144	145	146	147	148	149	150
151	152	153	154	155	156	157	158	159	160
161	162	163	164	165	166	167	168	169	170
171	172	173	174	175	176	177	178	179	180
181	182	183	184	185	186	187	188	189	190
191	192	193	194	195	196	197	198	199	200

Task A

1 What is the only even prime number?

2 Which columns have no prime numbers?

3 Which columns have no prime numbers in them after the first row?

4 How many prime numbers are there up to 100?

5 How many prime numbers are there between 100 and 200?

6 41 and 43 are a pair of consecutive odd numbers that are prime numbers. What other pairs like this can you find?

7 There are three numbers between 13 and 17.

There are five numbers between 47 and 53.

What is the largest gap between prime numbers that you can find in the table?

This is a multiplication grid

1	2	3	4	5	6	7	8	9	10	11	12	13	14	15	16	17	18	19	20
2	4	6	8	10	12	14	16	18	20	22	24	26	28	30	32	34	36	38	40
3	6	9	12	15	18	21	24	27	30	33	36	39	42	45	48	51	54	57	60
4	8	12	16	20	24	28	32	36	40	44	48	52	56	60	64	68	72	76	80
5	10	15	20	25	30	35	40	45	50	55	60	65	70	75	80	85	90	95	100
6	12	18	24	30	36	42	48	54	60	66	72	78	84	90	96	102	108	114	120
7	14	21	28	35	42	49	56	62	70	77	84	91	98	105	112	119	126	133	140
8	16	24	32	40	48	56	64	72	80	88	96	104	112	120	128	136	144	152	160
9	18	27	36	45	54	63	72	81	90	99	108	117	126	135	144	153	162	171	180
10	20	30	40	50	60	70	80	90	100	110	120	130	140	150	160	170	180	190	200
11	22	33	44	55	66	77	88	99	110	121	132	143	154	165	176	187	198	209	220
12	24	36	48	60	72	84	96	108	120	132	144	156	168	180	192	204	216	228	240
13	26	39	52	65	78	91	104	117	130	143	156	169	182	195	208	221	234	247	260
14	28	42	56	70	84	98	112	126	140	154	168	182	196	210	224	238	252	266	280
15	30	45	60	75	90	105	120	135	150	165	180	195	210	225	240	255	270	285	300
16	32	48	64	80	96	112	128	144	160	176	192	208	224	240	256	272	288	304	320
17	34	51	68	85	102	119	136	153	170	187	204	221	238	255	272	289	306	323	340
18	36	54	72	90	108	126	144	162	180	198	216	234	252	270	288	306	324	342	360
19	38	57	76	95	114	133	152	171	190	209	228	247	266	285	304	323	342	361	380
20	40	60	80	100	120	140	160	180	200	220	240	260	280	300	320	340	360	380	400

Task B

1 Shade or colour all the 24s.

2 Each time you shade a 24 you can find two factors
   by looking at the end of the row and column.
   What factors of 24 can you find by doing this?

3 Find factors of 30 in the same way.

4 Find factors of 60 in the same way.

5 Use your table to find numbers which appear to
   have a lot of factors.

6 The table shows that 91 is the product of two prime
   numbers. What are they?

7 Use the table to find other numbers which are the
   product of two prime factors.

   Hint: use the table of prime numbers to help you.

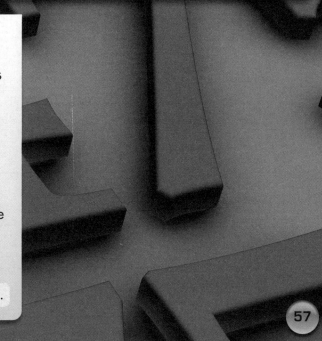

57

5 Statistics: Statistical charts and diagrams

5.1 Interpreting charts and diagrams

In this section you will learn how to:
- extract information from charts and diagrams.

Key words
bar chart
line graph
pictogram
pie chart
stem-and-leaf diagram

WORKED EXAMPLE

This line graph shows the average height of girls at different ages.

a Why is a line graph better than a bar chart for this information?

b What is the average gain in height from 12 to 16 years old?

c Estimate from the graph the average height of a 9-year-old girl.

d Why could the graph be misleading?

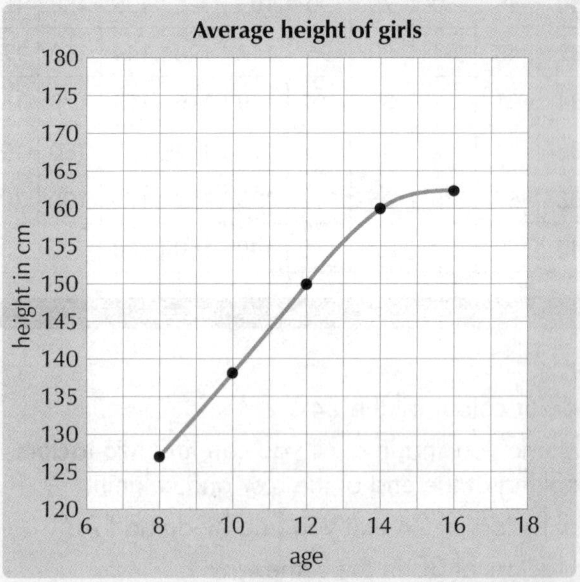

Average height of girls

(line graph: x-axis "age" from 6 to 18, y-axis "height in cm" from 120 to 180)

Solution

a A line graph is better when something is changing with time.

b The average height at 12 is 150 cm.

The average height at 16 is 162.5 cm. ——→ Read the scale carefully.

The gain in height is 162.5 − 150 = 12.5 cm.

c The average height of a 9 year old girl is ——→ This point has not been plotted but we about 132 or 133 cm.   can estimate from the line graph.

d The graph could be misleading because ——→ It looks as if height doubles from age 10 to the height scale does not start at 0.   age 12 but that is not true!

FM Functional Maths **AU** (AO2) Assessing Understanding **PS** (AO3) Problem Solving

EXERCISE 5A

FM **1** Monty compared car insurance prices. He looked at two types of insurance, comprehensive and third party. Here are the results for four companies.

Company	Comprehensive	Third Party
Alphasure	£280	£225
Easygo	£324	£247
Cheepy	£295	£219
Captain	£306	£253

a Which company was most expensive for comprehensive insurance?

_____

b Which company was most expensive for third party insurance?

_____

c What was the difference between the two Cheepy prices?

_____

d Which company would you recommend? Give a reason for your answer.

_____

2 This table shows the distances in kilometres between 5 cities.

a Write down the distance between Hull and Manchester.

_____ km   (1)

Hull

100	Leeds			
162	73	Manchester		
110	60	65	Sheffield	
63	40	118	95	York

b From the table, write down the name of the city which is

i nearest to Hull, _____

ii 60 km from Sheffield. _____   (2)

(Total 3 marks)

Edexcel, May 2008, Paper 1 Foundation, Question 6

3 This bar chart shows the estimated populations of six countries in northern Europe.

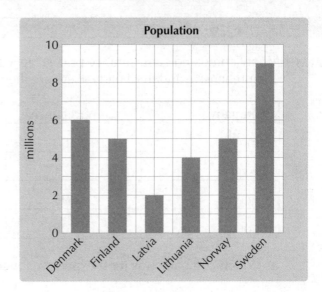

a Which country has the largest population?

_____

b Which countries have the same population?

_____

c What is the difference between the populations of Sweden and Latvia? _____

d What is the total population of the six countries? _____

e Compare the populations of Denmark and Lithuania.

_____

Hint: what are the populations? Which is larger? How much more?

4 The graph shows information about the rainfall in Kathmandu.

It shows the number of days it rained each month.

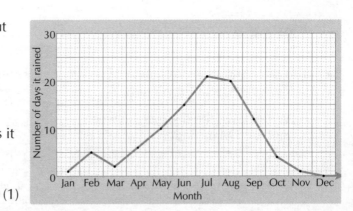

a Write down the number of days it rained in April.

_____ days   (1)

One month it rained on exactly 12 days.

b Which month? _____   (1)

(Total 2 marks)

Edexcel, March 2008, Paper 5/8 Foundation, Question 3

AU **5** Josie carried out a survey. She asked people to name their phone provider. She put the results in a spreadsheet and produced this chart.

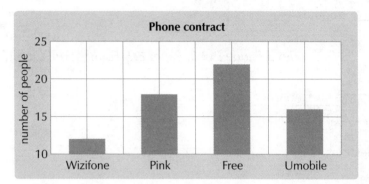

a Josie said the chart shows that the number using Free is about twice the number using Umobile. Do you agree? Explain your answer.

_____

b Why is the chart misleading?

_____

6 The bar chart shows information about the amount of time, in minutes, that Andrew and Karen spent watching television on four days last week.

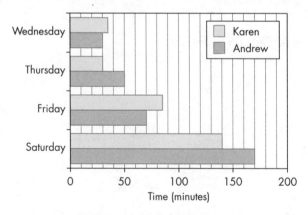

Karen spent more time watching television than Andrew on two of these days.

a Write down these days.

_____ and _____   (2)

b Work out the total amount of time Andrew spent watching television on these four days.

_____ minutes   (2)

(Total 4 marks)

Edexcel, June 2008, Paper 8/5 Foundation, Question 2

Extension

Work with a partner on these questions.

1 A survey was done of the ages of teachers in a school.

The results are in this **stem-and-leaf diagram**.

2	3	4	4	5	7			
3	0	0	2	4	5	5	7	7
4	1	5	5	5	7			
5	1	3	4	5	5	9		
6	0	4						

Key: 4 | 5 represents 45 years old.

a Check that **three** teachers in the survey are 45 years old.

b How many teachers in the survey are 37 years old? _____

c How many teachers are over 50 years old? _____

d How many teachers took part in the survey? _____

e What is the difference in age between the oldest and youngest teachers?

(This is the **range**.) _____

Show your working here.

5.2 Drawing charts and graphs

In this section you will learn how to:

● draw an appropriate chart or graph to illustrate data.

Key words

bar chart
line graph
pictogram
pie chart

WORKED EXAMPLE

Here are the medals two countries won in the 2008 Olympics.

Country	Gold	Silver	Bronze
Cuba	2	11	11
Kenya	5	5	5

a Draw a chart to show this.

b Explain your choice.

Solution

a A comparative bar chart would work well. You can do this on paper or from a spreadsheet.

b This is a good choice because you can easily see which country got more of each medal.

Can you think of a different way to draw a comparative bar chart?

You could put the Cuba columns together and put the Kenya columns together.

EXERCISE 5B

PS **1** Here are the results of a survey.

22 girls and 17 boys were asked about whether a party should be on Friday, Saturday or Sunday.

10 girls and 5 boys said Friday. 3 girls and 8 boys said Saturday. The rest said Sunday.

a Write the numbers in this table and complete it.

	Friday	**Saturday**	**Sunday**
Girls			
Boys			
Total			

b Which day was the most popular? _____

2 The pictogram shows the number of plates sold by a shop on Monday, Tuesday, Wednesday and Thursday of one week.

Monday	◯ ◯
Tuesday	◯ ◖
Wednesday	◯ ◯ ◯
Thursday	◯
Friday	
Saturday	

Key: ◯ represents 10 plates

a Work out the number of plates sold on Monday.

_____ (1)

b Work out the number of plates sold on Tuesday.

_____ (1)

The shop sold 40 plates of Friday.

The shop sold 25 plates on Saturday.

c Use this information to complete the pictogram. (2)

(Total 4 marks)

Edexcel, November 2008, Paper 2 Foundation, Question 1

3 Mr White recorded the number of students absent one week.

The dual bar chart shows this information for the first four days.

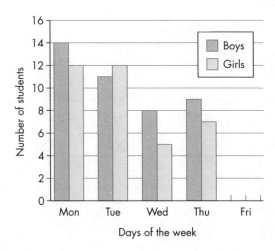

a How many boys were absent on Monday?

_____ (1)

b How many girls were absent on Wednesday?

_____ (1)

On Friday, 9 boys were absent and 6 girls were absent.

c Use this information to complete the bar chart. (2)

On only one day more girls were absent than boys.

d Which day? _____ (1)

(Total 5 marks)

Edexcel, March 2008, Paper 8/5 Foundation, Question 1

4 In the 2008 Olympics, Spain gained 5 gold, 10 silver and 3 bronze medals.

Label the slices of this pie chart with the medal colours.

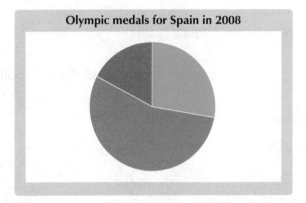

Olympic medals for Spain in 2008

AU 5 Here is the population of a town over a number of years.

Year	1950	1960	1970	1980	1990	2000
Population	8000	7500	6000	4500	7000	8500

a Complete this line graph.

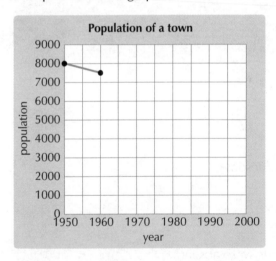

b Describe how the population has changed between 1950 and 2000.

_____

_____

_____

_____

1 In the 2008 Olympics, Turkey won 1 gold, 4 silver and 3 bronze medals.

Fill in this pie chart.

Hint: what fraction of the medals were silver?

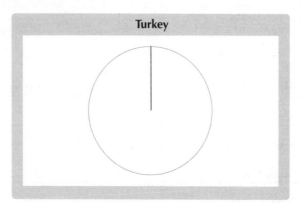

2 In the 2008 Olympics, Britain won 19 gold, 13 silver and 15 bronze medals.

a Draw a diagram to show this.

b Why did you choose to draw that type of diagram?

5.3 ## Using statistical charts and diagrams

In this section you will learn how to:
● interpret information in a real context and draw appropriate charts and graphs to illustrate it.

Key words
bar chart
data
pictogram
pie chart

WORKED EXAMPLE

This data sheet shows the energy, protein, carbohydrate and fat in 100 grams of seven different biscuits.

Energy is measured in Kilojoules (kJ). Protein, carbohydrate and fat are measured in grams (g).

You can find this information on any packet of biscuits.

Biscuit	Energy (kJ)	Protein (g)	Carbohydrate (g)	Fat (g)
Ginger nuts	1870	5	73	15
Custard creams	2130	5	67	25
Rich tea	1904	7	71	16
Cream crackers	1880	10	69	15
Oatcakes	1800	11	58	17
Breadsticks	1770	14	71	9
Crispbread	1580	16	70	4

Show the energy content of these biscuits in a suitable diagram.

Solution

A pictogram or a bar chart could be used.

A line graph or a pie chart are not good choices. ⎯⎯⎯⎯→ Why not? Because the data is not changing so a line graph would have no meaning between the plotted points, and a pie chart would not show the amount of energy in each biscuit.

This bar chart was drawn using a spreadsheet. You could also do it on squared paper.

The bars can be horizontal or vertical.

Be careful about choosing the scale to include all the numbers. A spreadsheet will do that for you!

Energy content of biscuits (kJ)

Crispbread

Breadsticks

Oatcakes

Cream crackers

Rich tea

Custard creams

Ginger nuts

0   500   1000 1500 2000 2500

EXERCISE 5C

Use the information in the data sheet in the example to answer these questions.

1 Which biscuit has the highest energy content? _____

2 Which biscuit has the lowest carbohydrate content? _____

3 How many biscuits have a carbohydrate content of over 70 g? _____

4 **a** Complete this bar chart to show the protein content of the biscuits.

b Which biscuit has twice the protein content of rich tea?

_____

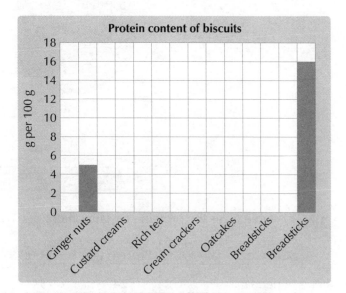

FM **5** **a** Complete this bar chart comparing the protein and fat content.

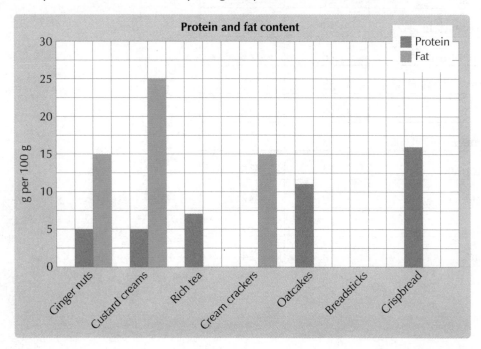

b Is it true that biscuits with more protein have more fat? Give a reason for your answer.

_____

6 This pie chart shows the protein, carbohydrate and fat content of ginger nuts. Label the three slices correctly.

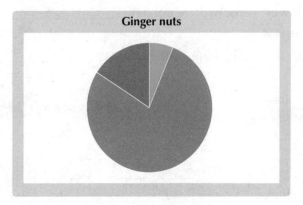

Ginger nuts

Extension

1 This table gives the protein and fat content per 100 g of 11 cheeses.

Cheese	Protein (g)	Fat (g)
Cheddar	24	34
Leicester	24	34
Wensleydale	23	31
Emmental	28	28
Edam	25	25
Brie	18	28
Parmesan	33	29
Stilton	22	36
Roquefort	18	32
Feta	16	23
Goat	15	24

a Here is a stem-and-leaf diagram for the protein.

```
1 | 5   6   8   8
2 | 2   3   4   4   5   8
3 | 3
```

Key: 2 | 4 represents 24 g

Check that this is correct. What is the difference between the largest and the smallest protein value? (This is called the **range**.)

_____

b Here is part of a stem-and-leaf diagram for the fat content. Complete the table.

```
2 | 3   4   5   8   8   9
3 |
```

Hint: make sure the numbers are in order and spaced out properly.

Hint: remember to put a key.

Departures

Task A

These timetables show the times of the first three trains from St Austell to Penzance and the times of three trains back again in the afternoon.

St Austell	1212	1337	1405
Truro	1230	1355	1423
Redruth	1242	1408	1436
Cambourne	1250	1414	1443
Penzance	1318	1439	1511

Penzance	1600	1644	1738
Cambourne	1623	1705	1803
Redruth	1630	1711	1810
Truro	1642	1724	1823
St Austell	1700	1741	1840

Look at the first train from St Austell to Penzance, which leaves at 1212.

1 How long is the journey between each station?
2 What is the total journey time?

Hugo and Mina live in St Austell. They want to go to Penzance for the afternoon.

They want to spend as long in Penzance as possible.
3 Which trains should they catch?
4 How long will they be able to spend in Penzance?

Task B

Northern Rail timetable

Carlisle	0944	Barrow-in-Furness	1712
Maryport	1021	Millom	1739
Whitehaven	1052	Ravenglass	1756
Ravenglass	1125	Whitehaven	1827
Millom	1144	Maryport	1855
Barrow-in-Furness	1216	Carlisle	1938

Ravenglass and Eskdale Railway timetable

Ravenglass	depart	1030	1110	1130	1150	1210	1250	1310
Eskdale	arrive	1110	1150	1210	1230	1250	1330	1414

Eskdale	depart	1510	1530	1550	1630	1650	1730	1815
Ravenglass	arrive	1550	1610	1630	1710	1730	1810	1850

Imagine you and some friends are on holiday in Carlisle.

You decide to visit Eskdale for the day, travelling by train.

You will catch the Northern Rail train from Carlisle to Ravenglass and then travel on the famous Ravenglass and Eskdale steam railway.

You want to spend as long as possible in Eskdale.

Use the timetables above to plan your journey.

1 Which trains should you catch and how long is each stage of the journey?

2 How long will you be able to spend in Eskdale?

Geometry and measures: Scale and drawing

6.1 Scale

In this section you will learn how to:
● read scales and estimate distances.

Key words
estimate
scale

WORKED EXAMPLE

This scale is marked in grams.

What is the weight shown on the scale?

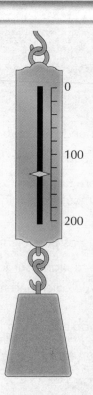

Solution

Look carefully at the scale.

There are five intervals between 0 and 100, so it must be going up in 20s. ⟶ 5 × 20 = 100

The pointer is halfway through the second interval after 100.

The weight is 100 + 20 + 10 = 130 g.

EXERCISE 6A

1 What temperatures are shown on these medical thermometers?

a _____

b _____

c _____

2 A normal body temperature is 37.0 °C.
A fever is a temperature of 37.7 °C or above.

Show these temperatures on the thermometers.

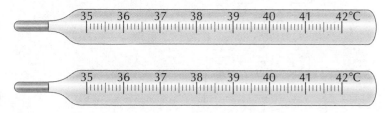

3 What speeds are shown on these car speedometers?

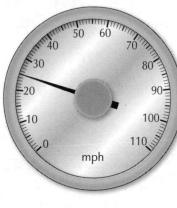  

a _____   b _____   c _____

4 This is part of a ruler.

a Write down the length marked with an arrow.

_____ cm   (1)

This is a thermometer.

b Write down the temperature shown.

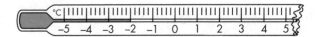

_____ °C   (1)

This is a parcel on some scales.

c Write down the weight of the parcel.

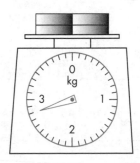

_____ kg   (1)

(Total 3 marks)

Edexcel, November 2007, Paper 10 Foundation, Unit 3 Test, Question 1

5 What quantity of liquid is shown in these jugs? Give your answers in ml.

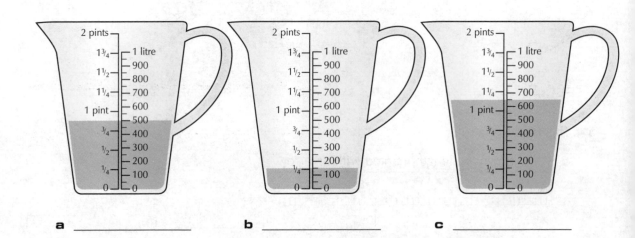

a _____   **b** _____   **c** _____

6 What is the quantity of liquid in these jugs? Give your answer in pints.

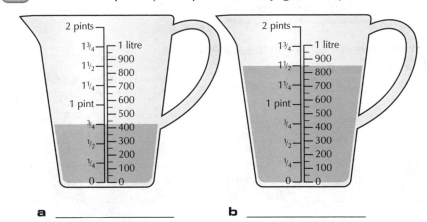

a _____

b _____

7 You will see scales like this in a post office. They are used to weigh parcels.

Find the weight shown on each one.

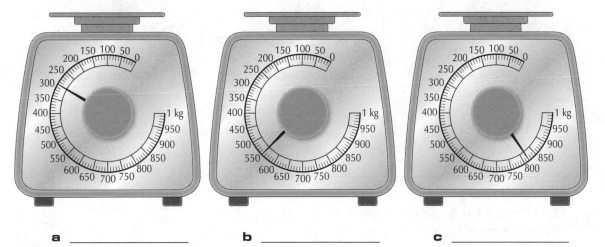

a _____

b _____

c _____

8 The car in this picture is 4 m long. Estimate the lengths of the bicycle and the bus.

Bicycle: _____ m   Bus: _____ m

AU 9 The standard height of a door is 2 m.
Estimate the height of the ceiling in the room you are in.   _____ m

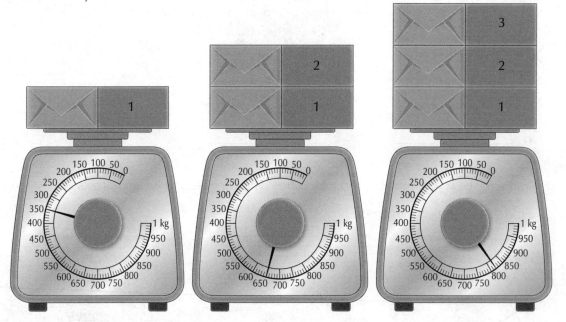

Extension

PS 1 Find the weight of each of the three parcels on the scales below.
Show how you found them.

_____

_____

AU 2 An old recipe has liquid quantities in pints and you
wish to change them to millilitres.

Use the scale on the jug to complete the table below.

Pints	$\frac{1}{4}$	$\frac{1}{2}$	$\frac{3}{4}$	1	$1\frac{1}{4}$
millilitres					

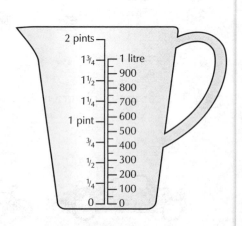

6.2 Nets

In this section you will learn how to:

● recognise nets of different 3D objects.

Key words

cube   pyramid
cuboid   prism
cylinder   net

WORKED EXAMPLE

Complete this net for a cuboid.

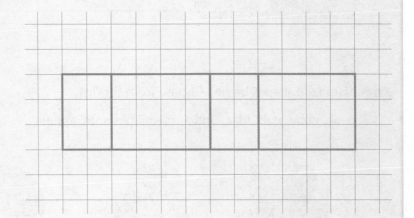

Solution

A cuboid is a rectangular box.

Four faces are shown and two are missing.

The four faces can fold up like this. ⟶ If you are unsure, cut out a copy on squared paper.

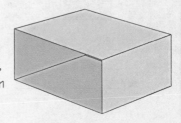

The missing faces are on the front and back.

You could add them like this: ⟶ There are other ways to do this.

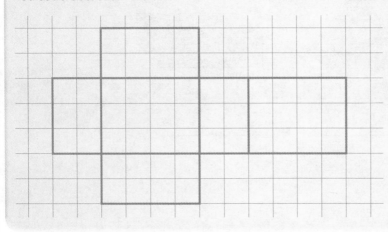

EXERCISE 6B

1 What is the mathematical name for the shape of a dice? _____

2 If you put three dice together like this, what shape do they make?

 _____

3 Name the shapes below. Choose from this list.

cone, cube, cuboid, cylinder, prism, pyramid, sphere

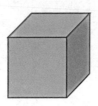   

a _____ **b** _____ **c** _____ **d** _____

  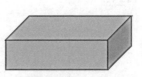

e _____ **f** _____ **g** _____

4 The diagram shows some nets and some solid shapes.
An arrow has been drawn from one net to its solid shape.

Draw an arrow from each of the other nets to its solid shape.

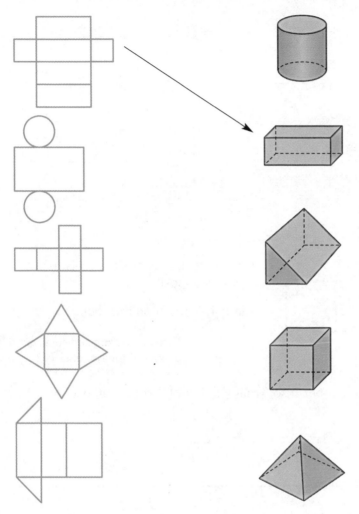

(Total 3 marks)

Edexcel, November 2008, Paper 13 Foundation, Question 5

AU 5 **a** What is the mathematical name for a baked bean can? _____

b A baked bean can is made out of three flat pieces of metal. What shapes are they?

_____

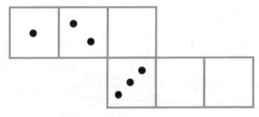

Extension

PS 1 Zelda drew this net of a pyramid.

Lucinda said it will not work. Why not?

_____

Hint: if you are not sure, try copying it and cutting it out.

PS 2 Here is a net for a dice.

On a dice, 6 is opposite 1, 5 is opposite 2, and 4 is opposite 3.

Mark 4, 5 and 6 on this dice.

Hint: if you are not sure, cut out a copy of the net and fold it up.

AU 3 Is it possible to draw a net for a cone? If so, what will it look like? If not, explain why not.

_____

_____

6.3 # Map scales

In this section you will learn how to:
● find distances on a map.

Key words
scale

WORKED EXAMPLE

These two cities are marked on a map with a scale of 1 cm to 20 km.

• Newingham

Birmcastle •

How far apart are they?

Solution

First measure the distance between them. ——————→ It is 12 cm.

The scale tells us that each centimetre represents 20 km on the ground.

The actual distance is 12 × 20 = 240 km.

EXERCISE 6C

1 These two villages are on a map with a scale of 1 cm to 1 mile.

Axton •

How far apart are the villages?

_____ miles

• Coldford

2 The scale of this map is 1 cm to 2 km.

windmill •   • tower

church •   • bridge

Find the distances between the following.

a The church and the windmill. _____ km

b The windmill and the tower. _____ km

c The tower and the bridge. _____ km

3 Power lines are to be laid from a power station to the points marked *A*, *B* and *C*.

• *C*

B •

• power station

A •

a Draw the lines of the cables on the map.

b The scale of the map is 1 cm to 10 miles. Find the total length of the three cables.

_____

PS 4 A map has a scale of 2 cm to 1 km.

You have been asked to write a table to convert map distances to distances on the ground. Put the missing numbers in this table. Add some more of your own.

On the map in cm	2 cm	10 cm				
On the ground in km						

5 A map has a scale of 2 cm to 1 km.
Here are some distances between places on the ground.
How far apart will they be on the map?

a 8 km _____ **b** 6.5 km _____ **c** 4.3 km _____ **d** 7.2 km _____

6 A road map has a scale of 1 cm to 20 km.
This scale can be used to convert map distances into distances on the ground.

a Fill in the missing kilometres.

b Convert these distances on the map into kilometres on the ground.

i 3 cm _____   **ii** 4.5 cm _____   **iii** 8.2 cm _____   **iv** 5.8 cm _____

Extension

PS **1** Here is a castle marked on a map. The scale is 1 cm to 2 km.

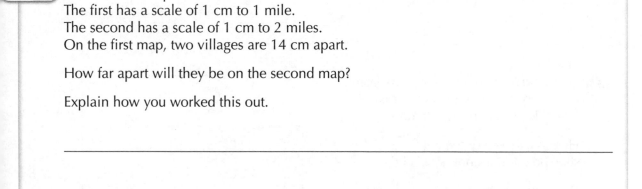

North

• castle

A station is 12 km east of the castle.

A café is 9 km south of the castle.

a Mark the station and the café on the map.

b How far apart are the station and the café?

_____ km

AU **2** Pete has two maps of the same location.
The first has a scale of 1 cm to 1 mile.
The second has a scale of 1 cm to 2 miles.
On the first map, two villages are 14 cm apart.

How far apart will they be on the second map?

Explain how you worked this out.

_____

_____

6.4 Using scales

In this section you will learn how to:
● use scales and interpret drawings in different contexts.

Key words
net
scale

EXERCISE 6D

FM 1 Ordnance Survey maps of the countryside use a scale of 1 to 25 000. They are very popular with walkers.

This means that 1 cm on the map represents $\frac{1}{4}$ of a kilometre.

a How many centimetres on the map represent 1 km? _____

b How many centimetres on the map represent 3 km? _____

c The distance between two hill tops on the map is 10 cm.
How far apart are the hill tops? _____

d Alan is planning a walk. He estimates the distance
on the map is 34 cm. How long is the walk? _____

e These maps have a square grid printed on them. The grid lines are 4 cm apart.
How will these help you judge distances when you are reading the map?

PS 2 The standard size for a shoe box from one famous shoe manufacturer is 32 cm by 17 cm by 12.5 cm.

Here is a sketch of the net for a shoe box. It does not have a lid.

Write the lengths on as many lines in this net as you can.

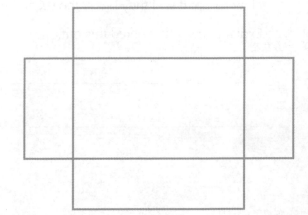

At the time of writing, the world triple jump record for men is 18.29 metres. Make a sketch with a man standing next to the length he completed. Say how you did it.

_____

_____

4 Roads in most European countries have speed limits given in km/h and not in mph. Car speedometers in the UK show both scales.

a This table shows speed limits in France in km/h. Use the speedometer to help you put in the corresponding speeds in mph.

	Motorway	Motorway when wet	Open road	Open road when wet	Dual carriageway	Dual carriageway when wet	Town
km/h	130	110	90	80	110	100	50
mph							

b How are speed limits in France different from speed limits in England?

_____

_____

Extension

1 Here are the heights of four famous structures.

Statue of Liberty in New York	92 metres
Eiffel Tower in Paris	300 metres
Leaning Tower of Pisa in Italy	55 metres
Great Pyramid of Giza in Egypt	147 metres

Hint: roughly how many times bigger is the Eiffel Tower than the Statue of Liberty?

On the opposite page, draw a sketch of each, side by side, to show their relative sizes.

checklist

☐ I can read scales and estimate distances.

☐ I can recognise nets of different 3D objects.

☐ I can find distances on a map.

☐ I can use scales and interpret drawings in different contexts.

You could work with a partner on this task.

A friend has asked you to help with the design for the back garden of a new house.

You need to include the following items in the design.

- A patio near the house, big enough for a table and chairs.
- A circular pond with a diameter of 2 metres.
- A section to grow vegetables that is at least 12 m^2 in area.
- A flower bed that is no wider than 1 metre.
- An area of grass with a children's slide on it.
- Paths that are 0.5 metres wide in suitable places.

The plot of land is 7 m wide and 10 m long.

The house is next to the shorter side.

Task

1   Make a scale drawing of a plan for the garden.

a   Start by working out the area of the piece of land.

b   Now draw a rectangle to represent the piece of land. Use a scale of 2 centimetres to 1 metre.

c   Now you can start your design. Make sure your design includes all the features in the white box.

   You will need to make some decisions for yourself. For example:

   –   Where is the best place to put the vegetable plot?

   –   How big does the patio need to be?

   –   How much room does the slide need?

   –   Where should any paths go?

   Include any relevant measurements on your plan.

2   When you have finished, compare your plan with someone else's. What are the similarities? What are the differences?

7 Measures: Units

Units of measurement

In this section you will learn how to:
- convert metric and non-metric units.

Key words

approximately
centimetre
gram
kilogram
kilometre
litre
metre
mile
millilitre
millimetre
pint
pound

You need to **remember** the conversions between these **metric units**.

10 mm = 1 cm	100 cm = 1 metre (m)	1000 m = 1 kilometre (km)
1000 mg = 1 gram (g)	1000 g = 1 kg	1000 kg = 1 tonne
1000 ml = 1 litre (l)		

Here are some useful conversions between **metric** units and **non-metric** units.

8 kilometres is approximately 5 miles
1 mile is approximately 1.6 kilometres
1 stone is approximately 6.3 kilograms

1 litre is approximately $1\frac{3}{4}$ pints
4 litres is approximately 7 pints
1 kilogram is approximately 2.2 pounds

WORKED EXAMPLE

In France, a road sign shows that the distance to Paris is 160 km. How many miles is that?

<u>Solution</u>

It is useful to remember that 8 km is approximately 5 miles.

So 80 km is approximately 50 miles ⟶ Multiplying by 10.

and 160 km is approximately 100 miles ⟶ Doubling the numbers.

You could also remember that 1 km is just over half a mile.

So 160 km will be a bit more than 80 miles. ⟶ 80 is half of 160.

This is less accurate but gives you a reasonable approximation to the answer.

FM Functional Maths **AU** (AO2) Assessing Understanding **PS** (AO3) Problem Solving

EXERCISE 7A

You can use a calculator if you wish.

1 Write down a sensible **metric** unit to measure the following.

   a The length of your foot _____

   b The capacity of a glass _____

   c The weight of a baby _____

   d The distance between two towns _____

   e The weight of a spoonful of sugar _____

   f The length of a room _____

2 Fill in the missing numbers.

   a 90 mm = _____ cm

   b 4 m = _____ cm

   c 2 km = _____ m

   d half a metre = _____ cm

   e half a kilometre = _____ m

   f 5.3 cm = _____ mm

3 Fill in the missing numbers.

   a 2 litres = _____ ml
   b half a litre = _____ ml
   c $\frac{1}{4}$ of a litre = _____ ml

4 **a** Complete the table by writing a sensible metric unit for each measurement.

   The first one has been done for you. (3)

The length of the river Nile	6700 kilometres
The height of the world's tallest tree	110 _____
The weight of a chicken's egg	70 _____
The amount of petrol in a full petrol tank of a car	40 _____

   b Change 4 metres to centimetres. _____ cm (1)

   c Change 1500 grams to kilograms. _____ kg (1)

(Total 5 marks)

Edexcel, May 2008, Paper 1 Foundation, Question 13

5 Write these lengths in metres.

a 3.5 km = _____ m   b 4.65 km = _____ m   c 0.35 km = _____ m

6 Write these quantities in ml.

a 1.5 litres = _____ ml   b 2.85 litres = _____ ml

c 0.61 litres = _____ ml

Some non-metric units are still in common use.
Miles, pints and stone (for weight) are three examples.

Hint: use the approximate conversions at the start of this section to calculate these.

7 Change these lengths to kilometres.

a 10 miles = _____ km   b 20 miles = _____ km

c 3 miles = _____ km

8 Change these quantities to pints.

a 2 litres = _____   b 8 litres = _____

c Is half a litre more or less than a pint? _____

9 People often know their weight in stones.

Change these weights to kilograms.

a 2 stones = _____   b 5 stones = _____   c 10 stones = _____

Extension

PS 1 A pint is exactly 576 ml.

a How many millilitres are in 2 pints? _____

b How many litres is that? _____

c A gallon is 8 pints. How many litres is 1 gallon? _____

AU **2** Work with a friend on this question.

The weight of a small car is about 1 tonne. Elephants weigh several tonnes.
A group of teenagers find that their total weight is exactly 1 tonne.

Estimate how many teenagers are in the group. Justify your answer.

_____

_____

7.2 Time and timetables

In this section you will learn how to:
- carry out calculations involving time and timetables.

Key words
24-hour clock

WORKED EXAMPLE

A train journey starts at 1735 and finishes at 2112. How long does it last?

<u>Solution</u>

The best way is counting on.

Method 1

1735 to 1800 is 25 minutes.

1800 to 2100 is 3 hours.

2100 to 2112 is 12 minutes.

The total time is 25 minutes + 3 hours + 12 minutes = 3 hours and 37 minutes.

Method 2

1735 to 2035 is 3 hours.

2035 to 2100 is 25 minutes.

2100 to 2112 is 12 minutes.

The total time is 3 hours + 25 minutes + 12 minutes = 3 hours and 37 minutes.

Be careful if you use a calculator. 2112 − 1735 will <u>not</u> give the correct answer because there are 60 minutes in an hour, not 100.

EXERCISE 7B

1 Bus and train timetables are written using the 24-hour clock.

9.30 am is written as 0930.   9.30 pm is written as 2130.

Change these to 24-hour clock times.

a 8.15 am is _____   **b** 1.20 pm is _____

c 5.00 pm is _____

2 If the clocks below show times in the morning, write them as 24-hour clock times.

a _____   **b** _____   **c** _____

3 If the clocks in question 2 show times in the afternoon or evening, write them as 24-hour clock times.

a _____   **b** _____   **c** _____

4 How long are these time intervals?

a 1500 to 1534 _____   **b** 0900 to 0909 _____

c 1340 to 1400 _____   **d** 1633 to 1700 _____

e 1805 to 1900 _____   **f** 0713 to 0800 _____

5 Here is part of a bus timetable.

a How frequently do buses leave Adderley?

_____

Adderley	1324	1354	1424	1454	1524
Binford	1345	1415	1445	1515	1545
Chatterton	1355	1425	1455	1525	1525
Denbigh	1411	1441	1511	1541	1541

How long do these journeys take?

b Adderley to Binford _____

c Binford to Chatterton _____

d Chatterton to Denbigh _____

e Adderley to Denbigh _____

Martin arrives at the Adderley bus stop at 2 pm.

f How long will he wait for a bus? _____

g He wants to get to Denbigh by 2.30 pm. How late will he be? _____

6 How long are these time intervals?

a 1015 to 1035 _____

b 1255 to 1310 _____

c 1930 to 2010 _____

d 0720 to 0820 _____

e 1610 to 1735 _____

f 1140 to 1315 _____

Extension

1 **a** A long train journey starts at 0943 and finishes at 1422.

How long did it take? _____

b Another train journey starts at 1325 and lasts 4 hours and 40 minutes.

At what time did it end? _____

c A third journey lasted two hours and thirty minutes and finished at 1115.

At what time did it start? _____

d Write your answers to **b** and **c** as 12-hour clock times using am or pm.

_____   _____

7.3 Units in action

In this section you will learn how to:
- use different units in real settings.

Key words
approximately

EXERCISE 7C

You may wish to use a calculator in this section.

1 Three of the races in the athletics in the Olympics are 1500 metres, 5000 metres and 10 000 metres. Write these lengths in kilometres.

_____

PS 2 You can buy milk in cartons in metric or non-metric measurements.

Put these four cartons in order of size, smallest first:

1 pint, 0.5 litres, 2 pints, 1 litre

_____

3 A magazine has an article about a woman who has been on a diet.
It says that she has reduced her weight from 14 stone to 10 stone.

a Approximately, what are those two weights in kilograms? _____

b How much weight did she lose (approximately) in kilograms? _____

4 Large juice cartons usually hold 1 litre.

Small individual juice cartons often hold 200 ml or 250 ml.

How many of these smaller cartons are equivalent to one large one?

_____

5 Sugar used to be sold in 2 pound bags. Now it is sold in 1 kg bags.

If 1 pound = 454 grams, what is the difference between those two weights?

_____

AU 6 Petrol used to be sold in gallons. Now it is sold in litres.

A litre is approximately 0.22 gallons.

A medium-sized car fuel tank has a capacity of about 50 litres. How many gallons is that?

_____

7 Here are the times for a train from Birmingham to Glasgow.

Birmingham	0920
Crewe	1009
Preston	1051
Carlisle	1200
Glasgow	1319

a How long is the whole journey?

_____

b The stops split the journey into four parts. How long will each part take?

_____

c Which pair of consecutive stations are likely to be the furthest apart?

_____

Extension

AU 1 A marathon is just over 26 miles long.

Roughly how many kilometres is that? _____

Hint: remember that 1 mile is approximately 1.6 km.

FM 2 Builders always put all lengths on plans and drawings in millimetres.

Change these dimensions into metres.

a The length of a room is 5400 mm _____

b The height of a ceiling is 2850 mm _____

c The length of a window is 1800 mm _____

d The height of a kitchen worktop is 930 mm _____

e Why do you think builders always write lengths in mm?

_____

_____

3 Here is part of a railway timetable.

Bristol Temple Meads	08 00	08 30	09 00
Bath	08 15	08 45	09 15
Chippenham	08 30	09 00	09 30
Swindon	08 50	09 20	09 50
Didcot	09 15	09 45	10 15
Reading	09 35	10 05	10 35
London Paddington	09 55	10 25	10 55

A train leaves from Bristol Temple Meads at 09 00

a At what time should the train arrive at Swindon? _____ (1)

Jambaya gets to the station in Chippenham at 08 45
She waits for the next train to Didcot.

b i How long should she have to wait? _____ minutes

ii At what time should she arrive at Didcot? _____ (2)

All the trains should take the same time to travel from Bath to Reading.

c How long, in minutes, should it take to travel from Bath to Reading?

_____ minutes (2)

(Total 5 marks)

Edexcel, June 2008, Paper 2 Foundation, Question 6

checklist

☐ I can convert metric and non-metric units.

☐ I can carry out calculations involving time and timetables.

☐ I can use different units in real settings.

You could work with a partner on these questions.

Metric units only came into regular use in England in the 20th century.

This section looks at some of the units that used to be used to measure length.

This railway bridge at Keynsham is 112 **miles** and 63 **chains** from Paddington station. Miles and chains were used to measure distances when the railways were built in the 19th Century.

Getting started

Did you know:
12 inches = 1 foot
3 feet = 1 yard
1760 yards = 1 mile

Have you heard of **chains** and **furlongs**?

1 furlong = 220 yards
The lengths of horse races are still usually given in furlongs. The posts along the track are called furlong posts, because they mark out this distance.

A furlong (a 'furrow length') was the distance a team of oxen could plough without resting.

1 chain = 22 yards
The distance between the wickets in a cricket match is one chain.

The chain takes its name from a real chain that was first used to survey land accurately in 1620 by Edmund Gunter.

Distances in chains are still found in many real estate records.

A chain is approximately 20 metres.

Task A

1 How many inches make one yard?
2 How many feet make one mile?
3 How many chains make one furlong?
4 How many furlongs make one mile?
5 What fraction of a mile is one furlong?
6 How many chains make one mile?

Task B

1 How many metres is a furlong?
2 How many furlongs make one kilometre?
3 Think of some distances around your school that could sensibly be measured in chains. Make a list of estimated distances.
4 Think of some distances in your neighbour-hood that could sensibly be measured in furlongs. Make a list of estimated distances.

A **quarter of a chain** has several names: a **rod**, a **pole**, or a **perch**. It was originally the length of the stick that a ploughboy used to control the oxen pulling the plough.

5 How many feet make one rod?
6 How many rods make one chain?

Task C

You have been given information about a number of old units of measurement including furlongs, chains and rods.

You have also been given the metric equivalents of some of them.

Construct a table that could be used to look up the connections between different old units and to find their approximate metric equivalents.

You might like to make this into a poster and include illustrations.

8 Geometry: Symmetry

8.1 Reflection symmetry

In this section you will learn how to:
- reflect a shape in a mirror line
- find lines of symmetry.

Key words
reflection
symmetry

WORKED EXAMPLE

How many lines of symmetry do a square and a parallelogram have?

Solution

Remember that if we fold a shape along a line of symmetry, the two parts will exactly match.

We can do that in four ways with a square.

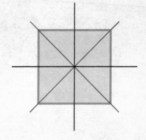

A square has **four** lines of symmetry. ⟶ You can check by folding a square of paper.

This is a parallelogram.

It has **no** lines of symmetry. ⟶ Do you disagree? Check by folding a parallelogram of paper.

EXERCISE 8A

1. Draw the lines of symmetry on the following shapes.

a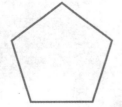

b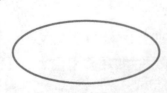

c

d  **e** 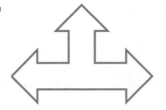 **f**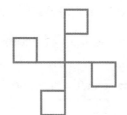

2 How many lines of symmetry do these icons have?

a 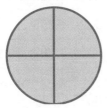   **b**    **c**

_____   _____   _____

3 Complete the shapes on the grid so that the black line is a line of symmetry.

a 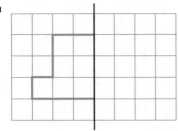   **b**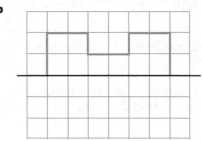

4 Draw the reflection of these shapes to make the blue and black lines into lines of symmetry and name the complete shapes.

a 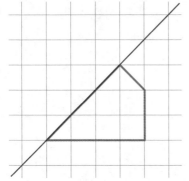   **b**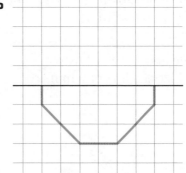

Name of the complete shape: Name of the complete shape:

_____   _____

5 Which of these letters have:

a no lines of symmetry? _____

b exactly one line of symmetry? _____ **c** two lines of symmetry? _____

SHAPE

6 This multiplication table is **symmetrical**.

Use the **symmetry** to fill in the missing numbers **without doing any calculations**.

Hint: the answers are right in front of you!

×	25	26	27	28	29
25	625	650	675	700	725
26	650	676	702	728	754
27	675		729	756	783
28	700			784	812
29	725				841

Extension

1 **a** Reflect the orange shape in the blue line.

b Reflect **both** parts in the black line.

c How many lines of symmetry does the finished shape have?

_____

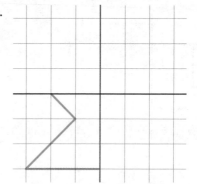

2 **a** Draw a horizontal line of symmetry through this word.

b Write another word with a horizontal line of symmetry.

_____

CODE

8.2 Rotation symmetry

In this section you will learn how to:
● recognise and describe rotational symmetry.

Key words
order
rotational symmetry

WORKED EXAMPLE

Describe the symmetry of this shape.

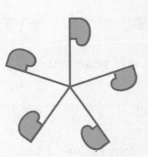

Solution

We can look for reflections or rotations.

It has no lines of symmetry.

It has rotational symmetry of order 5. ⟶ Check with a piece of tracing paper.

If you turn it around, it will match up five times in one whole turn.

EXERCISE 8B

1 What is the order of rotation of the following shapes?

Hint: shape **g** has order 1. We say it has no rotational symmetry.

a

order: _____

b

order: _____

c
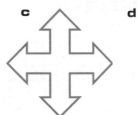
order: _____

d

order: _____

e

order: _____

f

order: _____

g
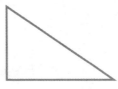
order: _____

h

order: _____

2 This shape has no rotational symmetry. The order of rotational symmetry is 1. Continue this drawing to make it have a rotational symmetry of order 4.

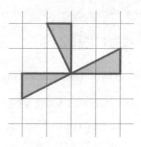

3 Here is a list of 8 numbers.

11	16	18	36	68	69	82	88

From these numbers, write down a number which has

a exactly one line of symmetry. _____ (1)

b 2 lines of symmetry *and* rotational symmetry of order 2. _____ (1)

c rotational symmetry of order 2 but *no* lines of symmetry. _____ (1)

(Total 3 marks)

Edexcel, Question 5d, Paper 1 Foundation, June 2005

4 a On the diagram below, shade **one** square so that the shape has exactly one line of symmetry.

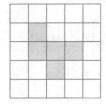

(1)

b On the diagram below, shade **one** square so that the shape has rotational symmetry of order 2.

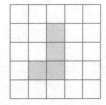

(1)

(Total 2 marks)

Edexcel, November 2008, Paper 1 Foundation, Question 10

5 For each of these letters, give the order of rotational symmetry and the number of lines of symmetry.

	Order of rotational symmetry	Lines of symmetry
S		
N		
W		
X		
Z		

Extension

AU 1 This word has rotational symmetry of order 2 but no lines of symmetry.

NOON

a Find other words with rotational symmetry and no line symmetry and words with line symmetry but no rotational symmetry.

_____

b Do you know any words which have both forms of symmetry?

_____

c Compare your results with other people's.

Hint: start with letters that look the same when you turn them upside down.

PS 2 Draw a picture that has:

• rotational symmetry of order 5

• no lines of symmetry.

Use this pentagon as a starting point.

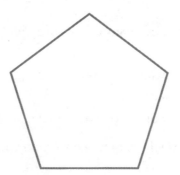

8.3 Symmetry in everyday situations

In this section you will learn how to:
● recognise different types of symmetry in realistic situations.

Key words
line of symmetry
order of rotational symmetry

EXERCISE 8C

1 You have probably seen this tangram puzzle before.

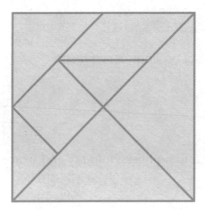

They have been used for thousands of years to help people practise their spatial understanding.

Seven pieces fit together to make a square.

Trace this shape onto a piece of paper and cut out the pieces.

a Which piece has four lines of symmetry?

_____

b Which piece has no lines of symmetry? _____

c Which **two** pieces have rotational symmetry? _____

d Use the cut out pieces to make another shape with rotational symmetry.

e Now use them to make a shape with line symmetry.

2 Here are some road signs

Draw in any lines of symmetry.

If it has rotational symmetry, write the order of rotational symmetry under it; otherwise write 'none'.

a

_____

b

_____

c

_____

d

_____

e

_____

f

_____

3 Here are two car logos. Do you recognise them?

a For each one find the number of lines of symmetry and the order of rotational symmetry (if any).

i

_____

_____

ii

_____

_____

b See if you can find any other symmetric car logos. Sketch them here and describe the symmetry.

_____

_____

Extension

AU 1 This is a tile.

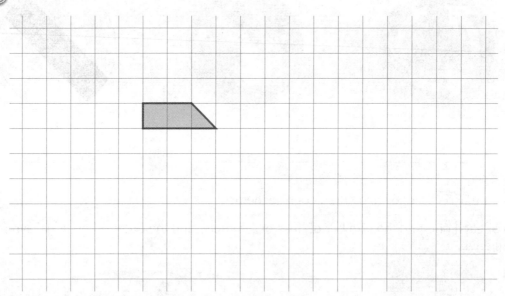

Use tiles of this shape to make a symmetrical pattern.

Describe the symmetry of your pattern.

_____

_____

Hint: does your pattern have lines of symmetry or rotational symmetry?

checklist

☐ I can reflect a shape in a mirror line.

☐ I can find lines of symmetry.

☐ I can recognise and describe rotational symmetry.

☐ I can recognise different types of symmetry in realistic situations.

You are a designer working for a leading car manufacturer. You have been set the task of designing the hub cap for a new model.

Task A

Carry out market research into existing hubcaps by recording the symmetry of these hubcaps in the table.

All of the hubcaps have rotational symmetry to make the wheel balanced. Some of them also have lines of symmetry.

Task B

Design a new hubcap for a leading car manufacturer. It must have rotational symmetry to ensure balance.

Hubcap	Order of rotational symmetry	Lines of symmetry
1 Vauxhall	9	9
2 Ford		
3 Hyundai		
4 Ford		
5 Vauxhall		
6 Renault		
7 Citroën		
8 Almeira		
9 Saab		
10 Ford		
11 Audi		
12 Renault		
13 Smart		
14 Ford		
15 Fiat		

1 Vauxhall

2 Ford

3 Hyundai

4 Ford

5 Vauxhall

6 Renault

7 Citroën

8 Almeira

9 Saab

10 Ford

11 Audi

12 Renault

13 Smart

14 Ford

15 Fiat

9 Algebra: Graphs and coordinates

9.1 Conversion graphs

In this section you will learn how to:
● read values from a conversion graph.

Key words
approximate
convert
graph
value

WORKED EXAMPLE

Older people tend to know their weight in stones but not in kilograms.

Here is a conversion chart.

a Stepan's granddad weighs 15 stones. What is that in kilograms?

b Stepan weighs 50 kilograms. What is that in stones?

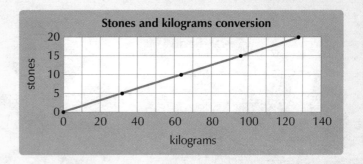

Solution

a Find 15 on the stones axis.

Read across to the line and down to the kilogram axis. ──→ Red arrows on diagram below.

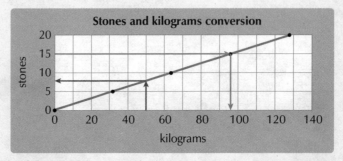

Be careful with the scale. 80 and 100 are marked.
The line between them must be 90.
The answer is about 96 kilograms. ───────────→ Any answer from a graph like this will be approximate and not exact.

b This time start at 50 on the kilogram axis ———————➤ Blue arrows on diagram.
and go up and across.

The answer is about 8 stone.

EXERCISE 9A

1 What numbers are these arrows pointing to?

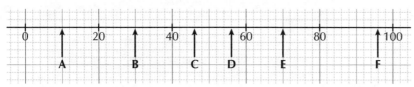

A = _____   B = _____   C = _____

D = _____   E = _____   F = _____

FM 2 Suppose you are on holiday in Italy.
The currency is euros.

This is a conversion graph.

a Complete these euro to pound conversions.

50 euros = _____

100 euros = _____

75 euros = _____

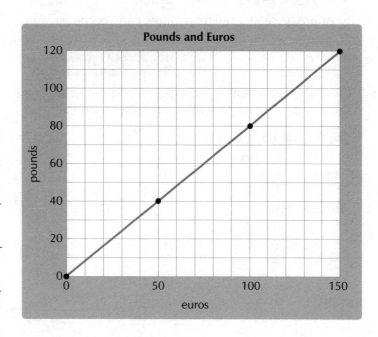

b You buy these items. Use the graph to estimate the prices in pounds as accurately as you can.

A meal for 40 euros = _____   A hotel room for 90 euros = _____

Sunglasses for 15 euros = _____   A coach trip for 65 euros = _____

FM 3 This graph shows the cost of petrol at a petrol station.

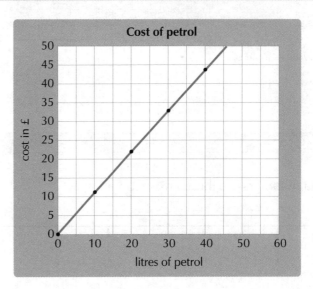

a Complete this table.

Litres	10	20	30	40
Cost in £				

b You have £40 to spend on petrol.

Approximately how many litres can you buy? _____

Extension

1 There are two temperature scales in common use, degrees F and degrees C. You can use this graph to convert between them.

Use the graph to convert these temperatures to degrees F.

Hint: be careful, the scales on each axis are different.

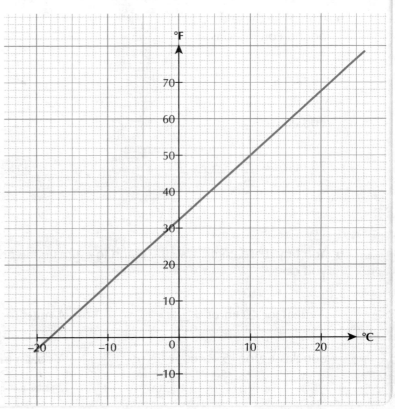

a 10 °C = _____ °F

b −10 °C = _____ °F

Use the graph to covert these temperatures to degrees C.

c 20 °F = _____ °C

d 0 °F = _____ °C

2 Bill uses this graph to work out an estimate for the cost, in £s, of diesel.

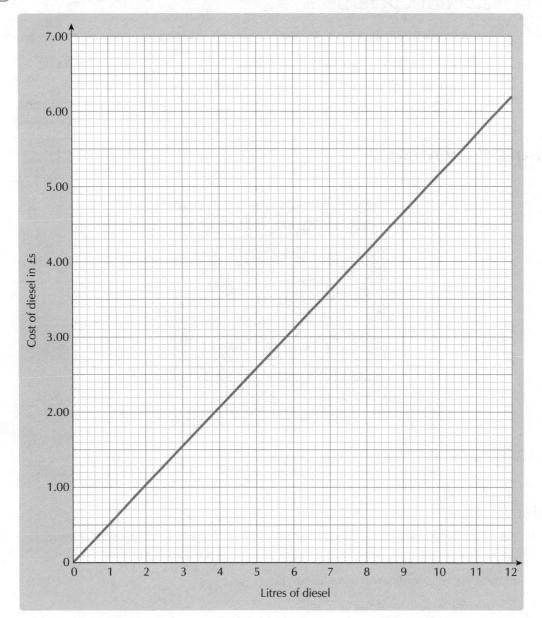

a How much does 6 litres of diesel cost?   £_____   (1)

b How much diesel can he buy for £3.50?   _____ litres   (1)

(Total 2 marks)

Edexcel, March 2008, Paper 10 Foundation, Question 5

9.2 Coordinates

In this section you will learn how to:
● use coordinates with positive and negative numbers.

Key words
coordinate
negative number

WORKED EXAMPLE

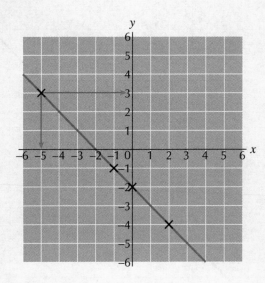

Write down the coordinates of the four points marked.

If the line is extended to go through the point (−20, *), what number does * stand for?

Solution

The points are (−5, 3), (−1, −1), (0, −2) and (2, −4). ⟶ Remember to write the *x* coordinate first. Look at the arrows.

Notice that each pair of coordinates adds up to −2.

That is, −5 + 3 = −2, −1 + −1 = −2, 0 + −2 = −2 and 2 + −4 = −2.

We can write this as $x + y = −2$.

So, if −20 + * = −2, then * must be 18.

EXERCISE 9B

The coordinates of *B* are (–3, 2).

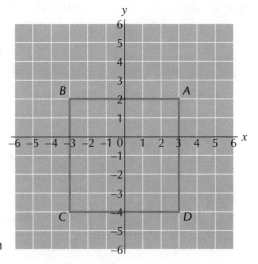

a Write down the coordinates of the other three corners of the square.

A _____

C _____

D _____

b The mid-point of *AB* is at (0, 2). Put a cross on this point and label it *F*.

c Put a cross on the mid-point of each of the other three sides of the square and label them with letters. (You choose the letters!)

Write down the coordinates of the three points.

_____

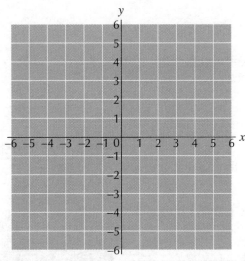

a Put these points on the grid and join them up in order.
(2, 1) (–2, 4) (–6, 1) (–6, –3) (–2, –6) (2, –3) (2, 1)

b You should have drawn a hexagon. Draw in the diagonals by joining opposite corners.

c Write down the coordinates of the point where the three diagonals meet.

_____

AU **3** **a** Write down the coordinates of point *P*.

(_____ , _____) (1)

b On the grid, mark the point (5, –2) with a cross (x). Label the point *Q*. (1)

c **i** On the grid, mark with a cross (x) the midpoint of the line *PR*.

ii Write down the coordinates of the midpoint of the line *PR*.

(_____ , _____) (2)

(Total 4 marks)

Edexcel, June 2008, Paper 10 Foundation, Question 5

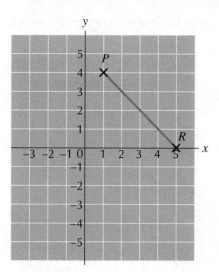

Extension

AU **1** **a** Plot the points (–3, 6), (–2, 5), (0, 3) and (4, –1).

b Draw a straight line through the points.

c Explain why *x* + *y* = 3 for the points on the line.

_____

_____

d If the line is extended to go through the point (20, *) what number does the * represent?

_____

9.3 Drawing graphs

In this section you will learn how to:
● draw a graph when you know its equation.

Key words
coordinates
equation
graph

WORKED EXAMPLE

Complete this table of values and use it to draw a graph of $y = 3x$.

x	−2	−1	0	1	2
$3x$					

Solution

Multiply each x value by 3. ————————→ Be careful with the negative numbers.

x	−2	−1	0	1	2
$3x$	−6	−3	0	3	6

We now have pairs of coordinates:

(−2, −6), (−1, −3), (0, 0), (1, 3) and
(2, 6).

Plot them on graph paper.
Join them up.

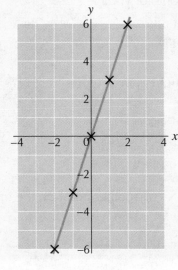

They should be in a straight line.
This is a way to check your answer.

EXERCISE 9C

1 **a** Complete this table of values.

x	0	1	2	3	4
$y = x + 2$				5	

b The table gives the coordinates of 5 points.

They are all on the line on this graph.

The equation of the graph is $y = x + 2$.

Mark each of the five points with a cross.

c Write down the coordinates of another point on the line.

_____

Check that $y = x + 2$. _____

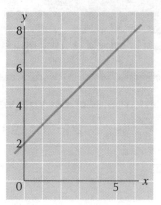

2 a Complete this table of values.

x	0	1	3	5	4
$2x$					

This gives you the coordinates of 5 points on the line $y = 2x$.

b Plot the points on the grid.
Two have already been done for you.

> **Hint:** always use a **pencil** to draw graphs, never use a pen.

c Join the points with a **straight** line.
Use a ruler and pencil.

> **Hint:** if they are not in a straight line you have made a mistake.

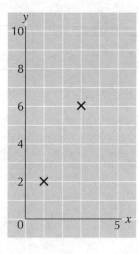

d Write down the coordinates of another point on the line. _____

Check that $y = 2x$. _____

3 a Complete this table of values.

x	2	4	5	6	8
$\frac{1}{2}x$					

b Use your table to draw a graph of $y = \frac{1}{2}x$.

> **Hint:** first mark the points with a cross. They should be in a straight line.

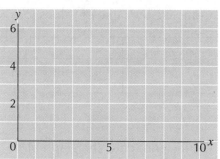

c Mark the points (10, 5) and (0, 0) on the grid. Extend your line through them if it does not already go that far.

d Write down the coordinates of another two points on the line.

_____ and _____

Extension

1 Complete this table. Use it to draw a graph of $y = 2x - 3$.

x	−1	0	1	2	3	4
2x − 3	−5					

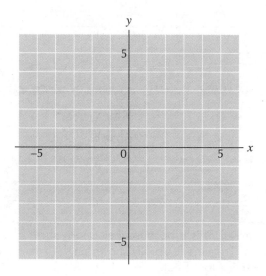

2 a Complete the table of values for $y = 3x - 1$

x	-2	-1	0	1	2
y		-4		2	

(2)

b On the grid, draw the graph of $y = 3x - 1$

(2)

(Total 4 marks)

Edexcel, March 2007, Paper 10 Foundation,
Question 6

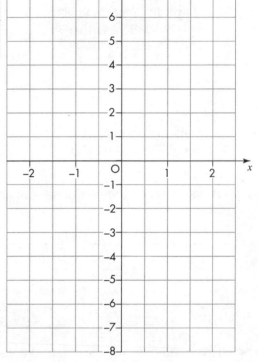

9.4 Real-life graphs

In this section you will learn how to:
● interpret graphs in real situations.

Key words
graph

EXERCISE 9D

Graphs are useful for telling stories, especially about travel. This is because they clearly show the distance travelled and the time taken at any point of the journey. The time is usually shown on the x-axis and the distance on the y-axis. When there is no movement the line looks flat.

1 Andy walked round to his friend's house.

Here is a graph of his journey.

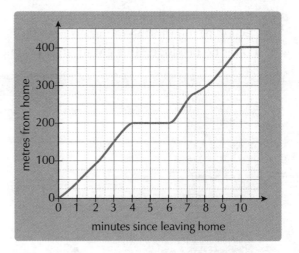

a His friend lives 400 metres away.
How long did the journey take?

_____

b Andy stopped on the way.
How long did he stop for?

_____

2 Kerim boiled some water in a kettle.
Here is a graph of the water temperature.

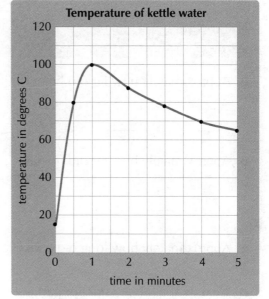

a What was the temperature of the water
at the start?

_____

b What was the temperature after
30 seconds?

_____

c How long did it take to boil?

_____

d What happened to the temperature after 1 minute? _____

e What was the temperature after 5 minutes? _____

3   Max was travelling on a motorway.
Every 30 minutes he recorded how far he had travelled.
Later he produced this graph on his computer.

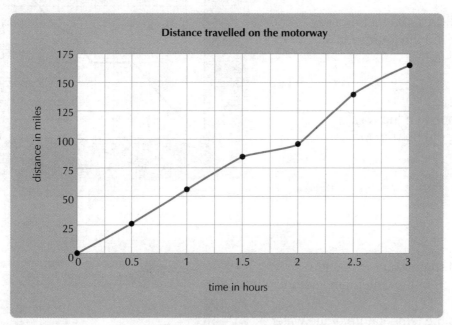

a Approximately how far did he travel in the first hour?

_____

b Approximately how far did he travel in three hours?

_____

c Approximately how long did it take to travel 100 miles? _____

d There was a lot of traffic for part of the journey and he had to slow down.

When did this happen? _____

e When was he travelling the fastest? _____

Hint: that is when the graph is steepest.

f The speed limit on the motorway is 70 miles per hour. Do you think Max was speeding for any part of the journey? Give a reason for your answer.

_____

_____

Extension

FM 1 A family are driving to visit some relatives. Here is a graph of their journey.

Describe their trip.

_____

_____

_____

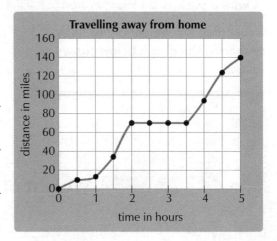

2 Here is a travel graph of Siân's journey from her house to the library and back to her house.

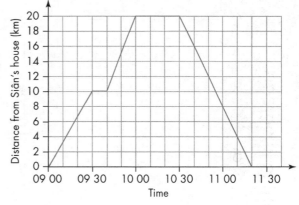

a How far is Siân from her house at 09 30?

_____ (1)

The library is 20 km from Siân's house.

b i At what time did Siân arrive at the library?

_____

ii How long did Siân spend at the library?_____ (2)

Siân left the library at 10 30 to travel back to her house.

c At what time did Siân arrive back at her house? _____ (1)

(Total 4 marks)

Edexcel, May 2008, Paper 12 Foundation, Question 10

checklist

☐ I can read values from a conversion graph.

☐ I can draw a graph when I know its equation.

☐ I can interpret graphs in real situations.

Functional Maths
Graph story

Work with a partner on this question.

Edith recorded the weight of her baby every month. The graph below shows the results.

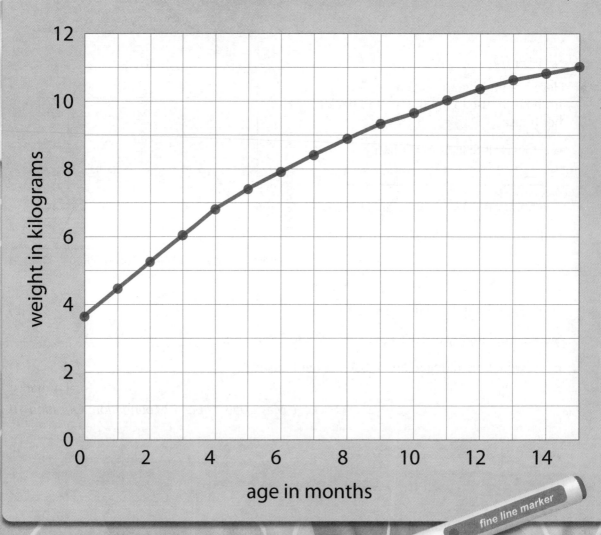

Weight of baby Jasmine

weight in kilograms

age in months

fine line marker

Getting started

Imagine that you are part of a team monitoring the growth of babies to ensure they are growing healthily.

You have been asked to write a brief report on how Jasmine's weight has increased over the first 15 months.

Task

Write your own report on Jasmine's progress.

Here are some things you could include.

- What was Jasmine's birth weight?
- What was her weight at particular ages, such as six months or one year?
- Did her weight increase at the same rate throughout the 15 months or did she put on weight more quickly at certain times?
- When did she reach particular weights, such as 5 kg or 10 kg?
- Were there any times when the weight dropped, which could indicate illness, or does Jasmine seem to be a healthy baby?
- 12-month-old girls are usually between 8.0 kg and 11.4 kg. Is there any evidence that Jasmine is overweight or underweight?

When you have finished writing your report, have a look at someone else's and compare it with your own.

10 Geometry and measures: Angles

10.1 Measuring angles

In this section you will learn how to:
- recognise, measure and draw angles.

Key words
acute
angle
obtuse
reflex

WORKED EXAMPLE

Measure the obtuse angle in this quadrilateral.

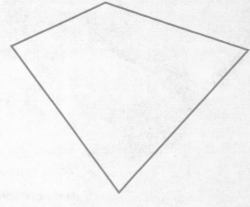

Solution

An obtuse angle is more than 90°.

In this shape it is the top one.

Place a protractor on the angle.

Choose the correct scale and read off the angle.

The obtuse angle is 138°.

> **Hint:** turn the book around, if it helps you to use the protractor.

An acute angle is less than 90°.

A reflex angle is more than 180°.

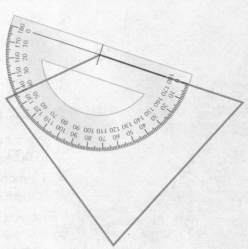

FM Functional Maths **AU** (AO2) Assessing Understanding **PS** (AO3) Problem Solving

EXERCISE 10A

1 Which of these are right angles? Circle the letters.

A   B   C   D

2 Which of the marked angles is an acute angle? _____ (1)

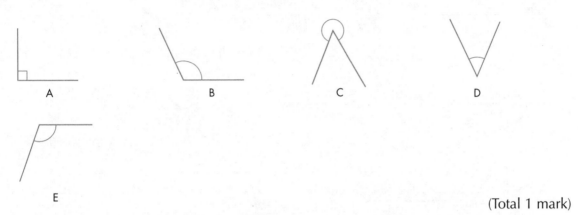

(Total 1 mark)

Edexcel, March 2009, Paper 7 Foundation, Unit 2 Stage 1, Question 5

3 Mark the obtuse angles inside this quadrilateral.

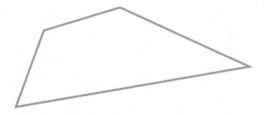

PS 4 List these angles in order of size, smallest first.

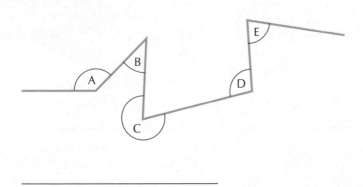

_____

5 Measure these angles.

a _____ °   **b** _____ °   **c** _____ °

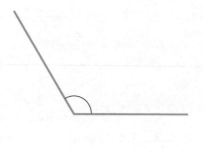

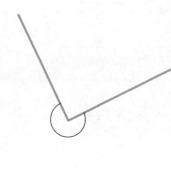

d _____ °   **e** _____ °   **f** _____ °

6 On one end of this line draw an angle of 45°.

On the other end draw an angle of 70°.

7 Draw angles of the following sizes.

a 55°   **b** 12°

c 120°   **d** 155°

Extension

AU 1 This triangle has three acute angles.

a Draw a triangle that has one obtuse angle.

b Can you draw a triangle with two obtuse angles?

_____

2 Draw a quadrilateral with one reflex angle.

10.2 Calculating angles

In this section you will learn how to:	Key words
● use known angles to calculate others.	angle quadrilateral

WORKED EXAMPLE

Calculate angle *a* in this diagram.

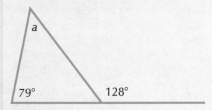

Solution

You must not try to measure it. The diagram is not accurately drawn.

First find the angle next to the 128° angle.

The angles on a straight line add up to 180 degrees. ———→ Important fact.

? = 180° − 128° = 52°

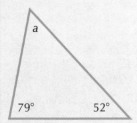

The angles of a triangle add up to 180 degrees. ———→ Another important fact.

79° + 52° = 131°

a = 180° − 131° = 49°

EXERCISE 10B

The diagrams in this exercise are not drawn accurately.

1 Calculate the lettered angles. **Hint:** the angles on a straight line add up to 180 degrees.

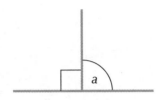 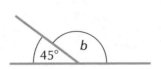 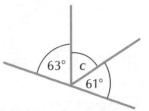

$a =$ _____ $b =$ _____ $c =$ _____

2 Calculate the lettered angles. **Hint:** the angles around a point add up to 360 degrees.

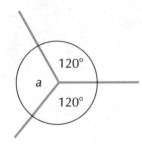 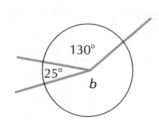 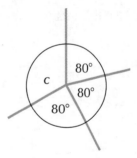

$a =$ _____ $b =$ _____ $c =$ _____

3 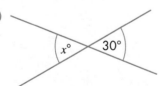 Diagram not drawn accurately

a i Write down the value of x. _____ (1)

ii Give a reason for your answer. _____

_____ (1)

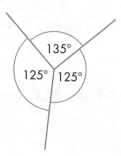

Diagram not drawn accurately

This diagram is wrong.

b Explain why. _____

_____

(1)

(Total 3 marks)

Edexcel, June 2008, Paper 2 Foundation, Question 14

4 The angles of any triangle add up to 180°.

Use this fact to calculate the unknown angles in these diagrams.

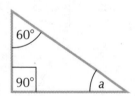

a = _____

b = _____

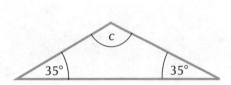

c = _____

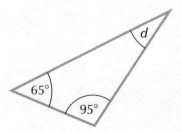

d = _____

Extension

1 **a** Measure the four angles in this quadrilateral and add them up.

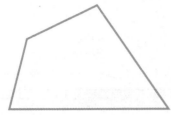

Total: _____

b Juno says that the four angles of a quadrilateral add up to 360°.

Do you think this is true?

_____

c The four angles of a quadrilateral do add up to 360°.
On a new piece of paper draw a quadrilateral of your own.
Add up the angles and see if your answer is close to 360°.

Compare your answer with your neighbour's.

AU **2** These three triangles are all congruent. That means they are the same size and shape.

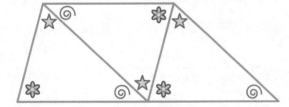

Can you see from this diagram why the three angles of the triangle must add up to 180°? Explain how you know.

_____

_____

_____

_____

10.3 Looking at angles

In this section you will learn how to:
● find angles in real situations and in patterns.

Key words
angle
tessellation

EXERCISE 10C

FM 1 The Health and Safety Executive says that the safe angle for a ladder is at 75° to the ground.

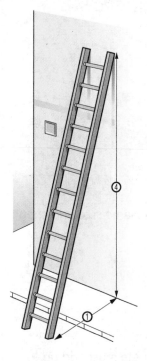

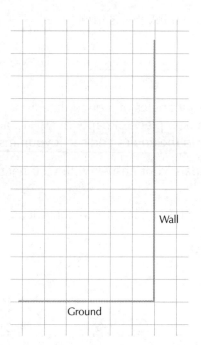

a Draw a diagram on the grid above to show a ladder leaning against a wall, measuring the 75° angle accurately.

b What is the angle between the ladder and the wall? _____

c The 'rule of 4' says that for a safe ladder, the height up the wall should be no more than four times the distance of the foot from the wall.

Check if this is true for your drawing.

2 You often see triangular frameworks in cranes and bridges.

FM

AU

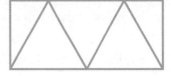

a How many equilateral triangles are in this framework?

_____

b Write in the sizes of all the angles within the framework.

c Why do you think triangles are used in frameworks instead of squares or some other shape?

_____

_____

AU **3** This is a tessellation of regular hexagons.

How does this show that every angle of a regular hexagon is 120°?

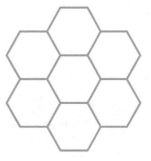

> **Hint:** look at the angles around one point.

_____

_____

You could work with a partner on this exercise.

1

AU

PS

Here is a regular octagon.

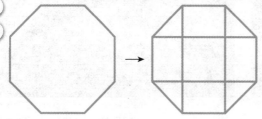

How big is each angle of the regular octagon? _____

Explain how you know. _____

_____

PS **2**

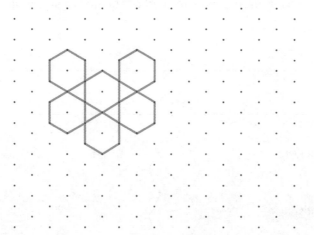

a What angles surround each point in this tessellation? Show that they add up to 360°.

_____

_____

b Extend the tessellation. Colour or shade the equilateral triangles.

checklist

☐ I can recognise, measure and draw angles.

☐ I can use known angles to calculate others.

☐ I can find angles in real situations and in patterns.

You could work with a partner on this activity.

This is a 30-60-90 triangle.
The angles are 30°, 60° and 90°.

In this activity you will see what other shapes you can make with 30-60-90 triangles.

You will need to make drawings of all the shapes you make.

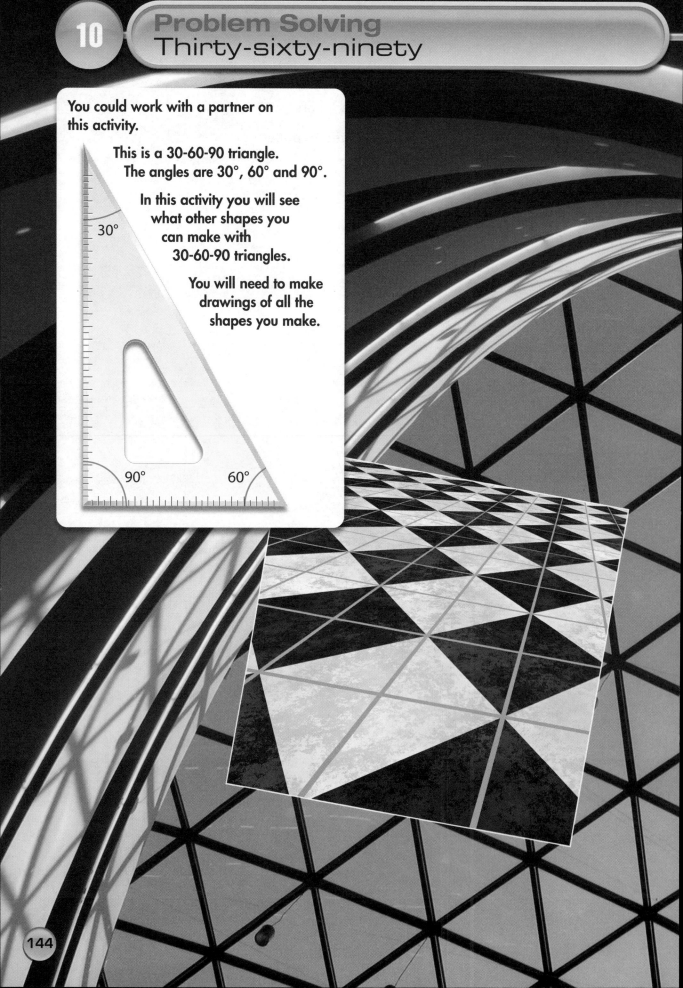

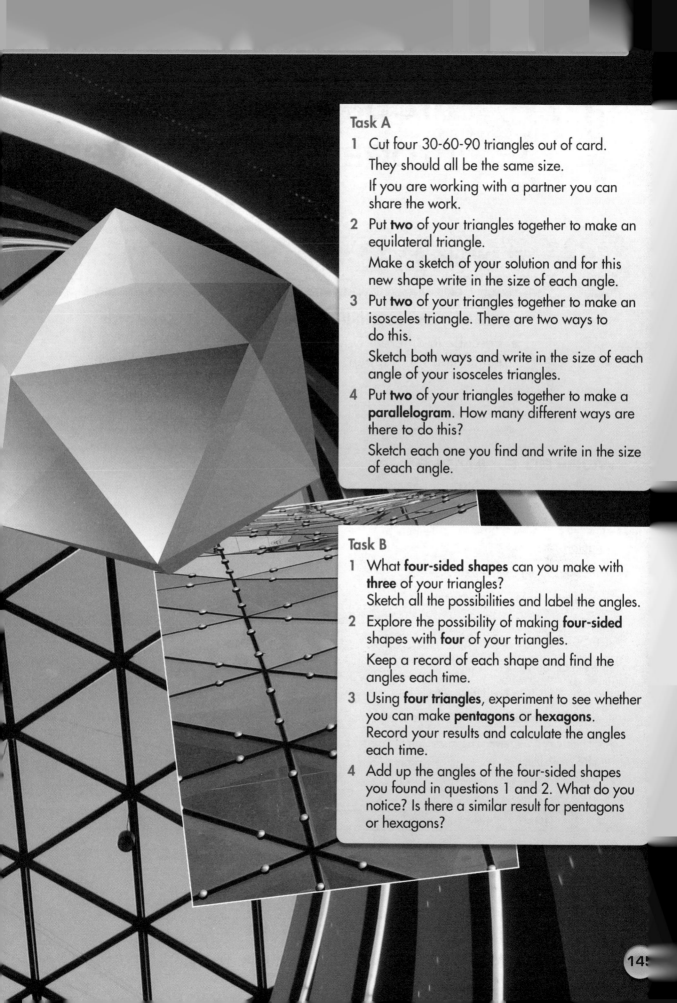

Task A

1. Cut four 30-60-90 triangles out of card. They should all be the same size. If you are working with a partner you can share the work.

2. Put **two** of your triangles together to make an equilateral triangle.

   Make a sketch of your solution and for this new shape write in the size of each angle.

3. Put **two** of your triangles together to make an isosceles triangle. There are two ways to do this.

   Sketch both ways and write in the size of each angle of your isosceles triangles.

4. Put **two** of your triangles together to make a **parallelogram**. How many different ways are there to do this?

   Sketch each one you find and write in the size of each angle.

Task B

1. What **four-sided shapes** can you make with **three** of your triangles?
   Sketch all the possibilities and label the angles.

2. Explore the possibility of making **four-sided** shapes with **four** of your triangles.

   Keep a record of each shape and find the angles each time.

3. Using **four triangles**, experiment to see whether you can make **pentagons** or **hexagons**.
   Record your results and calculate the angles each time.

4. Add up the angles of the four-sided shapes you found in questions 1 and 2. What do you notice? Is there a similar result for pentagons or hexagons?

11 Probability: Probability and events

11.1 Is it likely?

In this section you will learn how to:
- describe in different ways the chance that something will happen.

Key words
certain
even chance
likely
probability
unlikely

WORKED EXAMPLE

Ralph deals out the cards in a pack.

What is the probability that the third card he deals is a heart?

Solution

There are 13 hearts in a pack.

There are 52 cards all together.

So the probability is $\frac{13}{52}$. $\longrightarrow$ Always write a probability as a fraction, a decimal or a percentage

This simplifies to $\frac{1}{4}$.

The fact that it is the **third** card is not relevant.

It would be the same for the first or the second or any other.

Another way to answer the question is to say that there are 4 suits and hearts is 1 of them, so the probability is $\frac{1}{4}$.

EXERCISE 11A

1. Describe these events using one of these words.

impossible   unlikely   even chance   likely   certain

a A new-born baby will be a boy. _____

FM Functional Maths **AU** (AO2) Assessing Understanding **PS** (AO3) Problem Solving

b Chelsea will beat Manchester United 5-0. _____

c It will rain in the first two weeks of November. _____

d The sun will rise tomorrow. _____

e A car travelling at 100 mph will be caught for speeding. _____

f The first card dealt from a pack will be red. _____

g You will eat not chips in the next seven days. _____

h You can light a candle underwater. _____

2 The diagram shows some letters on cards.

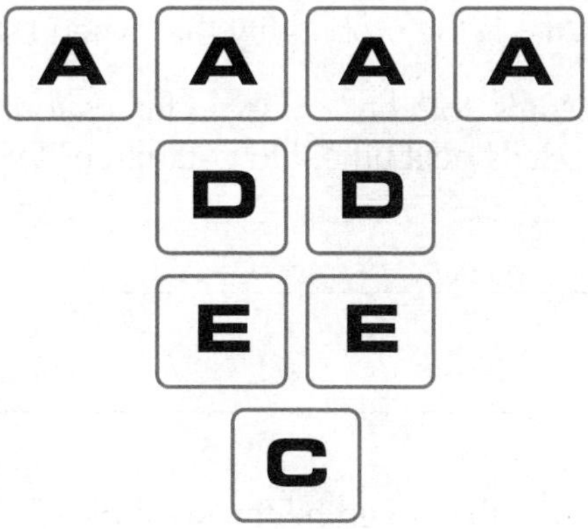

A A A A

D D

E E

C

Tamara takes a card at random.

a Which letter is **most** likely to be on the card? _____ (1)

b Which letter is **least likely** to be on the card? _____ (1)

(Total 2 marks)

Edexcel, March 2008, Paper 8/5 Foundation, Question 1

3 Match each statement to a letter on the probability scale below.

impossible ├─────┼───┼─────────┼────┼─────────────┤ certain
　　　　　　　A　　B　　　　　C　　D　　　　　　E

The first day of March in 2050 will be a Sunday. _____

The next king of the UK will be a man. _____

A dice will show 3, 4, 5 or 6 when rolled. _____

The Atlantic Ocean will freeze over next winter. _____

The score when a dice is thrown will be an even number. _____

AU 4 Discuss this question with a partner. You may not have the same answers.

Mark these events where you think they should be on the probability line below.

a It will be sunny tomorrow.

b It will rain next weekend.

c The next person who comes into the room will be female.

d You will be late for a lesson in the next week.

e You will go shopping for clothes in the next week.

f You will do some cooking in the next week.

impossible |——————————————————————————| certain

5 a What is the probability that when Esme spins a coin it will come up heads? _____

b Jason's coin has come up heads four times in a row. He says it is more likely to come up tails next time. Do you agree? Explain your answer.

_____

_____

6 Luis says that when he throws a dice, either it will be a 6 or it will not, so the probability that it will be a 6 is $\frac{1}{2}$.

What can you say to convince Luis that he is incorrect?

_____

_____

7 There are eight marbles in a bag.
Four marbles are blue (B),
two marbles are red (R)
and two marbles are green (G).

Steve takes a marble at random from the bag.

a On the probability scale, mark with the letter B, the probability that Steve will take a blue marble.

|———————————————|———————————————|
0                                $\frac{1}{2}$ 1

(1)

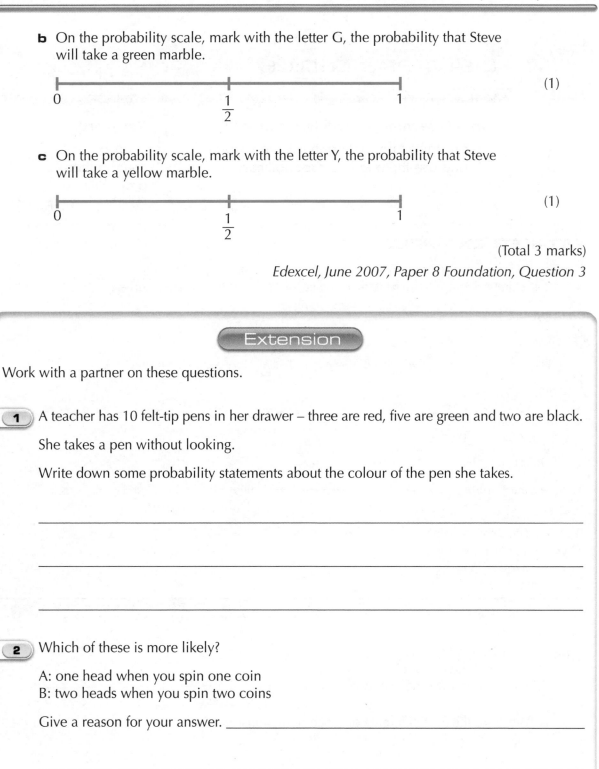

b On the probability scale, mark with the letter G, the probability that Steve will take a green marble.

(1)

0   $\frac{1}{2}$ 1

c On the probability scale, mark with the letter Y, the probability that Steve will take a yellow marble.

(1)

0   $\frac{1}{2}$ 1

(Total 3 marks)

Edexcel, June 2007, Paper 8 Foundation, Question 3

Extension

Work with a partner on these questions.

AU 1 A teacher has 10 felt-tip pens in her drawer – three are red, five are green and two are black.

She takes a pen without looking.

Write down some probability statements about the colour of the pen she takes.

_____

_____

_____

AU 2 Which of these is more likely?

A: one head when you spin one coin
B: two heads when you spin two coins

Give a reason for your answer. _____

_____

11.2 Lists and tables

In this section you will learn how to:
● organise information in lists and tables and use them to find probabilities.

Key words
chance
combination
probability

WORKED EXAMPLE

There are four teams in the semi-finals of a knockout football cup competition.
What is the probability that two particular teams will be drawn to play one another?

<u>Solution</u>

Call the teams A, B, C and D.

To find the probability that A will play B, we need to list all the possible combinations.

They are

A v B and C v D ⟶ Once A v B is chosen, the other pair is fixed.

or A v C and B v D

or A v D and B v C

We have clearly found all the possibilities. ⟶ A must play B, C or D and we have included each of those in turn.

There are three combinations,
so the probability that A plays B is $\frac{1}{3}$.

EXERCISE 11B

1 Kerim is designing a logo using two colours.
The logo will be red or blue.
The background will be yellow or green.

a What are the four different colour combinations?

_____

b Using the letter R, B, Y and G for the four colours, we can write one combination as RY.

How can we write the other three? _____

c Kerim decides he could use orange (O) as a logo colour.

List the new combinations available. _____

2 Olivia is on an activity holiday.
The table shows the activities available
on Wednesday and Thursday.

She must choose **one** activity on each day.

Wednesday	Thursday
River rafting (R)	Fishing (F)
Archery (A)	Walking (W)
Cycling (C)	Potholing (P)

a List all the possible combinations. Use the letters in brackets.

_____

_____

b How many combinations are there? _____

c She finds that one of the options on each day is full.
How many possible combinations does she have now? _____

3 Iqbal eats in a cafe.

He can choose **one** main course and **one** piece of fruit.

Main Course	Fruit
Fish	Apple
Lamb	Banana
Salad	Pear

One possible combination is (Fish, Pear).

Write down all the possible combinations that Iqbal can choose.

The first one has been done for you.

(F,P)

_____

(Total 2 marks)

Edexcel, March 2008, Paper 8/5 Foundation, Question 2

Extension

1 Noware United football team have played 12 games, won 6 and drawn 2.
Noware City have played 10, won 2 and drawn 3.

a Complete this table.

	won	drawn	lost	played
Noware United				
Noware City				
Total				

b Billie went to see one Noware United game.
What is the probability that they lost that game? _____

PS 2 Three men and three women are to be paired off in a ballroom dancing competition.

How many different ways are there to do this? Justify your answer.

_____

_____

11.3 Using probability

In this section you will learn how to:
● recognise and use probabilities in real life situations.

Key words
chance
probability

EXERCISE 11C

FM 1 Weather forecasters sometimes use percentages when they make a forecast.
Here is an example: "There is a 10% chance of rain tomorrow."

Does that mean that rain is likely? What does it mean?

_____

_____

FM 2 At the start of a cricket match, an umpire spins a coin to decide which side has the choice of batting or fielding first. Is this a fair method?

_____

3 People sometimes say, "If you drop a piece of buttered toast, it will always land with the buttered side down."

a Write this as a statement using the word **probability**.

_____

_____

b Do you think it is true? Explain your answer.

_____

_____

AU 4 "Why, sometimes I've believed as many as six impossible things before breakfast," said the White Queen in _Alice through the Looking-Glass_.

Suggest a couple of impossible things for her to believe before breakfast.

_____

_____

5 In the game of Tell Me (invented in 1933), a spinner can point to one of 22 letters of the alphabet (J, Q, X and Z are excluded).
The player must think of a word in a given category starting with that letter.

What is the probability that the letter is:

a the letter C? _____   **b** a letter in the word TODAY? _____

c a letter in the word BANANA? _____   **d** the letter X? _____

e a vowel? _____

f Why do you think four letters have been left out?

_____

AU 6 Work with a partner on this question.

Some board games involve throwing two dice and moving around a board a distance given by the total of the two dice.

Are all totals for two dice equally likely, or are some more likely than others? Explain your answer.

> **Hint:** if you are not sure, experiment with a pair of dice.

_____

_____

_____

_____

Extension

1 Answer this question with a partner.

In the National Lottery 'Lotto' draw, 7 balls (6 main balls and 1 bonus ball) are chosen out of 49 balls numbered 1 to 49.

Explain why the probability that any particular ball is chosen is $\frac{1}{7}$.

_____

_____

2 On the National Lottery website, you can check the frequency with which any ball has appeared in a particular period of time.

These results were found for a period of one year:

Most likely ball	39	Appeared in 23% of draws
Least likely ball	22	Appeared in 6% of draws

Say whether you agree with each of these statements. Give a reason for your answer each time.

a The number 39 appeared in nearly a quarter of the draws in the previous year.

_____

b The number 39 appeared nearly four times more than the number 22.

_____

c The number 22 is more likely to come up than other numbers in the next few weeks.

_____

d The number 22 is less likely to come up than other numbers in the next few weeks.

_____

e The Lotto draw is biased.

_____

If you have access to the Internet, you can check the latest frequencies for **39** and **22**. Are they still the most likely and least likely numbers?

checklist

☐ I can describe the chance that something will happen in different ways.

☐ I can organise information in lists and tables and use them to find probabilities.

☐ I can recognise and use probabilities in realistic situations.

The Human Fruit Machine is a popular stall at summer fêtes.

Three people sit in separate cubicles and all hold up a fruit at a given time, after a player has paid for a go. If the three pieces of fruit are a winning combination then the player wins a prize.

Getting started

You have been asked to organise a Human Fruit Machine stall at your local summer fête.

The problem is setting the prizes so that the game is attractive to play but still makes a profit.

After working through these exercises you should be able to decide how to do this.

Task A

First of all, suppose there are three people and just two types of fruit, apples and bananas. We will make the following assumptions.

- Each person chooses a fruit at random.
- No one can see what the others are choosing.
- The charge for one go is 20p.

1 One possible outcome is that they all choose an apple. We can write this as AAA.

   There are seven other outcomes.
   Can you list them all?

2 We will assume that all eight outcomes are equally likely. What is the probability of getting the outcome AAA?

3 Suppose there is one winning line, AAA.

   Explain why, on average, there will be one win in every eight plays.

4 If you win £1 for the winning line, is the game likely to make a profit or a loss?
   Give a reason for your answer.

5 If you win £2 for the winning line, is the game likely to make a profit or a loss?
   Give a reason for your answer.

6 Would you want to play the game if you could win £100 for the winning line?

Task B

Investigate what will happen with three fruit. How much could be offered as a prize whilst still making a profit?

12 Geometry: Transformations

12.1 | Congruent shapes

In this section you will learn how to:
- recognise congruent shapes.

Key words
congruent
enlargement
reflection

WORKED EXAMPLE

Which of the shapes in this rectangle are congruent?

Solution

There are two congruent right-angled triangles. (R)

There are two congruent parallelograms. (P)

There are two congruent trapeziums. (T)

There are two other triangles which are congruent. (O)

They are labelled in this diagram.

The remaining two shapes are not congruent. ———→ You can check these by copying them on paper and cutting them out.

Sometimes you need to turn one over to match them up.

FM Functional Maths   **AU** (AO2) Assessing Understanding   **PS** (AO3) Problem Solving

EXERCISE 12A

1 Two shapes are **congruent** if they are identical. One could be placed exactly on top of the other.

Three of these rectangles are congruent. Which is the odd one out? Why?

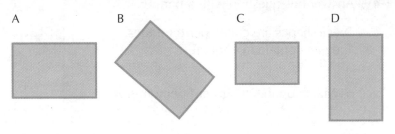

The odd one out is _____ because _____

2 **a** Match the pairs of congruent triangles.

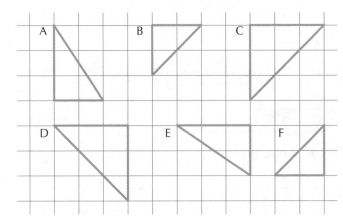

_____ and _____

_____ and _____

_____ and _____

b Which triangles are isosceles? _____

3 Here are some triangles.

  a Write down the letter of the triangle that is

    i right-angled, _____

    ii isosceles. _____ (2)

Two of the triangles are congruent.

  b Write down the letters of these two triangles.

    _____ and _____ (1)

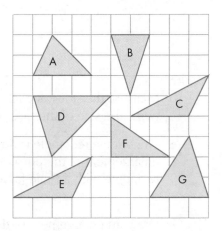

(Total 3 marks)

Edexcel, June 2008, Paper 13 Foundation, Question 1

159

AU 4 Answer this question with a partner.

These shapes are called **pentominoes**.
They all contain five squares.

a Match up the **congruent** pentominoes.

_____

_____

_____

Hint: if you are not sure, copy the shapes and cut them out.

b Which is the odd one out? Why? _____

Hint: colour congruent pentominoes in the same way.

Extension

1 **a** Explain why these rectangles are **not** congruent.

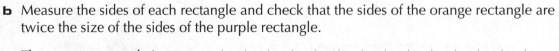

_____

_____

b Measure the sides of each rectangle and check that the sides of the orange rectangle are twice the size of the sides of the purple rectangle.

c The orange rectangle is an enlargement of the purple rectangle with a scale factor of 2.

Draw an enlargement of this triangle with a scale factor of 2.

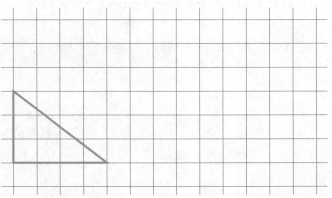

2 Draw your own example of an enlargement.

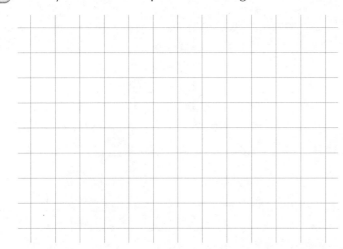

12.2 Putting shapes together

In this section you will learn how to:
- fit shapes together in tessellations.

Key words
congruent
tessellation

WORKED EXAMPLE

Show how to make a tessellation from this shape.

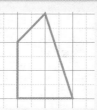

Solution

First rotate the original tile by half a turn.

Now repeat these two tiles.

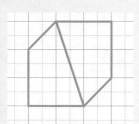

We can repeat this for as long as we wish.

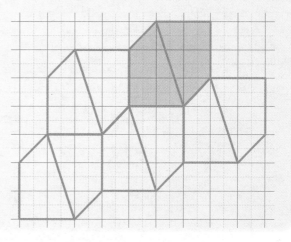

EXERCISE 12B

1. Here is one way to divide a square into four congruent parts.

Show two other ways to divide a square into four congruent parts.

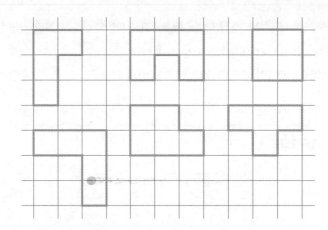

2. Show how these shapes could be put together to make three congruent squares.

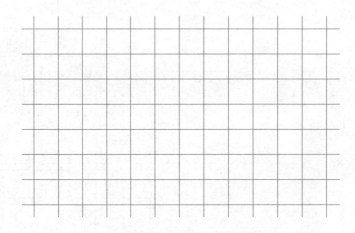

AU 3 A trapezium is being used to make a regular pattern.

A pattern like this is called a **tessellation**.

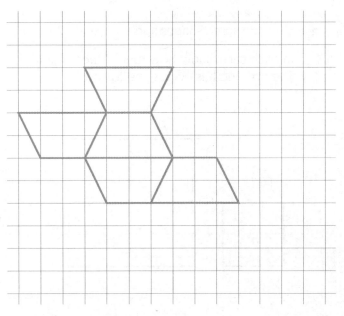

a Show how the pattern could continue.

b Bathroom, kitchen and floor tiles are usually square or rectangular.

Could trapezium-shaped tiles be used?

_____

c Why do you think trapezium-shaped tiles are not used? _____

_____

Extension

PS 1 This is the start of a tessellation. The four coloured tiles are all congruent.

Continue the pattern and colour it in.

Hint: use the lines to help you.

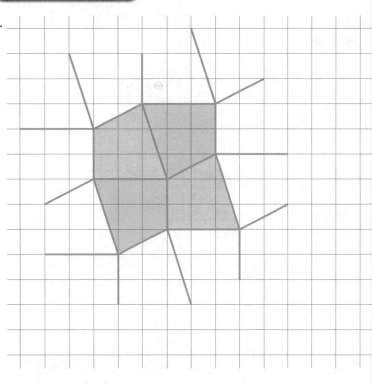

2 Here are some shapes and their scale 2 enlargements.

In each case, show how four of the original shapes will fit in the enlargement. The first one has been done for you.

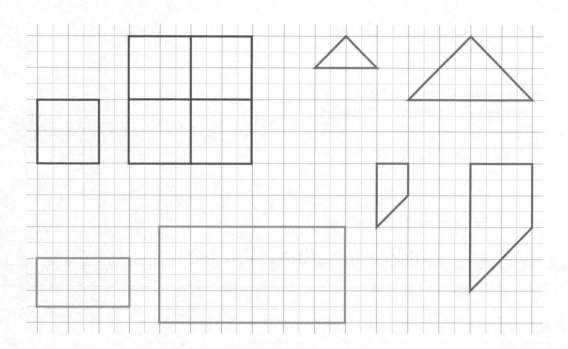

3 Show how to fit four of the shape on the left into the square on the right .

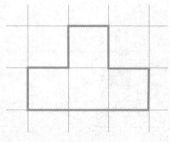 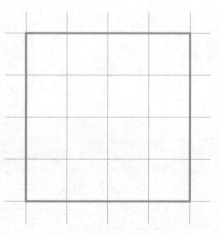

12.3 Using patterns from simple shapes

In this section you will learn how to:
- identify patterns in everyday situations.

Key words
congruent
tessellation

EXERCISE 12C

1 A farmer has an orchard with 12 trees.

She wants to leave it to her four daughters so that each one has the same shaped piece of land and the same number of trees.

Show on the diagram how she can do this.

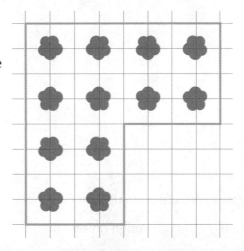

2 This is called a herringbone pattern.
It can be found in brickwork or in cloth.

This is the start of a herringbone pattern.

Continue the pattern.

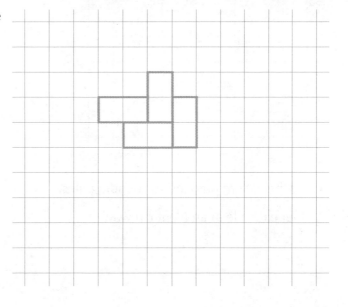

FM **3** A patio is to be covered with a mixture of square and octagonal tiles.

It will start like this.

Help the owner of the house to get an idea of what it will look like when finished by continuing the pattern.

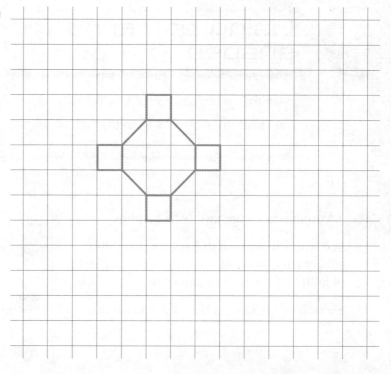

4 Square tiles are often designed to show a pattern when they are put together.

Here is a simple design on one tile.

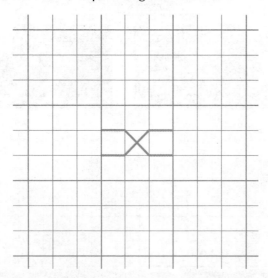

Copy the pattern onto the surrounding tiles.

Colour each tile in an identical way.

Extension

1 Make up your own tile design
and repeat it in each large square.

Colour each tile in an identical way.

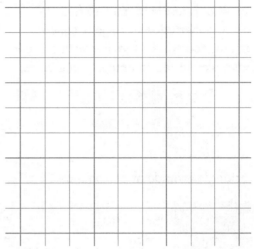

2 This design was found on a textile made in Japan in the 18th century.

a What symmetry does this design have? _____

b This design is repeated across the whole of the Japanese textile.
Show how this could be done.

checklist

☐ I can recognise congruent shapes.

☐ I can fit shapes together in tessellations.

☐ I can identify patterns in everyday situations.

You could work with a partner on this task.

A shape that is made by putting five squares together edge-to-edge is called a pentomino. You will be familiar with these if you have played the computer game Tetris.

Task A

This rectangle is made of pentominoes.

A B C D

E F G H

I

J

K L

In the rectangle there are six different pentominoes.
E and F are **not** different because they are **congruent**.
If you turn E over you can put it on top of F.

1 Match up the congruent pentominoes in the rectangle.
   If you are not sure cut some out of paper to check.
2 Which are the two which are not congruent to any others?

Task B

1 It is possible to make 12 different pentominoes. Can you find them all?

2 Which pentominoes look the **same** when you turn them over?

Here is a 5 by 6 rectangle. It has been filled with six copies of a single pentomino.

3 What other pentominoes can be used to fill the 5 by 6 rectangle **on their own**? Draw your own grids like the one below and make drawings to show how this can be done.

Task C

Here are two pentominoes.

1 Show how pentominoes of these two shapes **together** can fill a 5 by 6 rectangle.

2 What other **pairs** of pentominoes can be used together to fill a 5 by 6 rectangle? Make drawings to show how.

3 Can you fill a 5 by 6 rectangle with six **different** pentominoes?

4 A manufacturer wants to make a pentomino puzzle.

It will have the 12 different pentominoes made out of plastic.

He wants to fit them into a 6 by 10 rectangular box (like the rectangle in Task A).

The trouble is he cannot find a way to fit them in! Can you help?

Hint: this is not easy! You may want to cut out copies of the 12 pentominoes to experiment with.

Glossary

24-hour clock When time is told in the number of hours in the 24-hour day. The morning or AM hours are from 01h00 (the hour after midnight) to 12h00 (noon or midday). Then the afternoon and night, or PM hours start as 13h00, 14h00 … up to 24h00 (midnight).

acute angle An angle that is less than 90°.

add (*add* is a verb; *addition* is the noun) A basic operation of arithmetic, shown by a plus (+) sign. To add, or addition, is the process of combining two or more values to find their total value. For example, $2 + 3 = 5$.

angle The space, usually measured in degrees (°) between two straight lines that have a common endpoint (intersecting lines). The amount of turn needed to move from one line to the other.

approximate A value that is not exact, but is accurate enough for the situation. For example, one could say 'approximately 1000 people took part in the survey' rather than '989 people took part'.

bar chart A diagram, also known as a bar graph, that uses rectangular bars to show the size of a value. The bars can be vertical (going up) or horizontal (from side to side). (See also *graph*.)

bearing The direction relative to a line or fixed point.

brackets Symbols that are used to separate part of an expression, shown by: '(' and ')'. When a number or value is placed just outside a bracket in an equation, the two should be multiplied. For example, $3(5b + 1) = 15b + 3$.

cancel A fraction can be simplified by dividing the numerator and denominator by a common factor, called cancelling. For example, $\frac{10}{20} = \frac{5}{10} = \frac{1}{2}$. (See also *denominator*.)

centimetre A metric unit of length. One hundredth of a metre (0.001). 100 cm = 1 m.

certain When something is definite. For example, if an event is definitely going to occur, the probability that it will occur = 1. (See also *probability*.)

chance The probability (likelihood or possibility) of something happening. For example, there's a chance that it will rain today.

clockwise Turning in the same direction as the movement of the hands of a clock. (Taps are closed by turning them clockwise.)

combination A group or collection of things, in which the order does not matter. For example, four Aces in a game of cards.

congruent Exactly alike in shape and size.

consecutive Next to each other. For example, Monday and Tuesday are consecutive days, 7 and 8 are consecutive numbers.

convert To change something from one form to another. For example, from metres to centimetres. Or to change the way something is expressed. For example, from a fraction to a decimal: $\frac{1}{2} = 0.5$.

coordinate A set of values to show an exact position or point. For example, when looking at a map or graph you may be given point (10, 6): 10 shows the distance along and 6 shows the distance up or down.

cube 1. A 3D shape with six identical square faces. 2. The result of raising a number to the power of three. For example, 'two cubed' is written: 2^3, which is $2 \times 2 \times 2 = 8$.

cube number The result of raising a number to the power of three. For example, 'two cubed' is written: 2^3, which is $2 \times 2 \times 2 = 8$.

cuboid A box-shaped, solid object with faces that are all rectangles. It has six flat sides and all angles are right angles.

cylinder A solid or hollow prism with circular ends and uniform (unchanging) cross-section. The shape of a can of baked beans or a length of drainpipe.

data Information collected during a survey.

denominator The number under a fraction line. For example, the 3 of $\frac{1}{3}$. Here, the denominator tells you that it is divided into thirds.

difference The result of subtracting two numbers. For example, $10 - 7 = 3$, The difference between 10 and 7 is 3.

direction 1. The way something is facing or pointing. Direction can be described using the compass points (north, south, west, east) or using bearings (the clockwise angle turned from facing north). 2. Directions can also be: up, down, left and right.

divide (*divide* is a verb; *division* is the noun) A basic operation of arithmetic, shown by a division (÷) sign. To split into equal groups or parts, or to 'share fairly'. For example, how can 3 friends share 6 slices of pizza? (6 ÷ 3 = 2 slices each)

enlargement To make an object larger, in proportion to its original size (also known as a transformation).

equation A number sentence in which one side is equal to the other. An equation always contains an equals sign (=). For example, $9 + 4 = 8 + 5$.

equivalent The same, equal in value. For example, equivalent fractions are $\frac{1}{2} = \frac{3}{6}$.

estimate To guess a value close to the actual value by using some calculation. For example, the student estimated, by counting rows, that there were 360 apples in the box (9 by 10 rows in the top layers, and about 4 layers deep = $9 \times 10 \times 4$).

even chance An even number of times of the likelihood, or probability, of an event occurring. For example, the two people have an even chance of winning.

factor A whole number that divides exactly into a given number. For example, factors of 12 are 1, 2, 3, 4, 6 and 12.

fraction A fraction means 'part of something'. For example $\frac{1}{5}$. The whole amount is divided into equal parts (in this case 5). A fraction has a number on top (numerator) and a number at the bottom (denominator).

gram (abbreviation: g) A metric unit of mass. (See also *kilogram*.)

graph Values illustrated on a diagram; can be shown in various ways, but usually as lines or bars.

kilogram (abbreviation: kg) A metric unit of mass. A bag of sugar may have a mass of 1 kg. 1 kilogram = 1000 grams. (See also *gram*.)

kilometre (abbreviation: km) A metric unit of distance. 1 kilometre = 1000 metres.

likely If an event is likely to take place, there is a good chance that it will take place.

line graph A graph constructed by joining a number of points together.

line of symmetry A mirror line, or line of reflection; a line that divides something in half so that both sides are the same.

litre (abbreviation: l) A metric measure of volume or capacity. 1 litre = 1000 millilitres = 1000 cubic centimetres.

metre (abbreviation: m) A metric unit of length. 1 metre is approximately the arm span of a man. 1 metre = 100 centimetres

mile An imperial unit of length. One mile is almost 2 km. 1 mile = 1760 yards.

millilitre (abbreviation: ml) A metric unit of volume or capacity. One thousandth of a litre. 1000 ml = 1 litre.

millimetre (abbreviation: mm) A metric unit of length. One thousandth of a metre. 1000 mm = 1 metre.

multiple The multiples of a number are found by multiplying by a whole number. For example, $6 \times 5 = 30$. In this case, 30 is a multiple of 6 and of 5. Other multiples are 1, 3 and 10. Multiples of 8 are 1, 2, 4 and 8, 16, 24, 32 …

multiply (*multiply* is a verb; *multiplication* is the noun) A basic operation of arithmetic, shown by a multiplication (×) sign. Multiplication is associated with repeated addition. For example, $3 \times 9 = 9 + 9 + 9 = 27$.

negative number A number that is less than zero.

net A 2D pattern that you can fold to make a model of a 3D object. For example, a box that has been taken apart carefully and flattened forms a net.

obtuse angle An angle that is greater than 90° but less than 180°.

operation A mathematical process such as adding, subtracting, multiplying or dividing (+ − × ÷).

order Arranged according to a rule. For example, ascending order means from lowest to highest.

order of rotational symmetry A shape or pattern can be rotated about a fixed point. If it must be turned through a full circle before the picture looks the same as when it started, it has an order of rotation of one. If it looks the same two or three times during the complete rotation, it has an order of rotation of two or three.

pictogram Representation of data in a graph using pictures or symbols. For example, the number of potatoes sold over three months can be represented using kilogram bags of potatoes and portions of them.

pie chart A chart that represents data as slices of a whole 'pie' or circle. The circle is divided into sections. The number of degrees in the angle at the centre of each section represents the frequency. (See also *frequency*.)

pint An imperial unit of volume or capacity. 1 pint is just over half a litre. Milk is usually sold in 1-pint or 2-pint cartons. 8 pints = 1 gallon.

place value The value of a digit in a number, depending upon its place: units, tens, hundreds, thousands, etc. For example, in 273, the place value of 2 is hundreds, of 7 it is tens and of 3 it is units.

pound An imperial unit of mass. 1 pound is 454 g. (Also: 1 pound = 16 ounces, 14 pounds = 1 stone.)

prime number A number whose only factors are 1 and itself. For example, 17 is a prime number because it can only be divided evenly by 1 or 17. Note: 1 is not a prime number; 2 is the only even prime number. (See also *factor*.)

prism A 3D shape with two identical ends and flat (or perpendicular) sides, all the same length.

probability The measure of the possibility or likelihood of an event occurring.

product The result of multiplying two or more numbers or expressions together. For example, the product of multiplying: $2 \times 32 = 64$, or $2a \times b = 2ab$.

pyramid A polyhedron on a triangular base, with triangular faces meeting at a vertex.

quadrilateral A flat shape, or polygon, with four flat sides. For example: square, rectangle, parallelogram, kite, trapezium.

reflection The image formed after being reflected. The process of reflecting an object.

reflex angle An angle that is greater than 180° and less than 360°.

rotational symmetry A shape which can be turned about a point so that it coincides exactly with its original position at least twice in a complete rotation. (See also *order of rotational symmetry*.)

round To approximate a number so that it is accurate enough for a specific purpose. The number may be slightly reduced or increased. For example, 368 rounded to the nearest 10 = 370.

scale A scale on a diagram shows the scale factor (or ratio of the length) used to make the drawing. The axes on a graph or chart will use a scale depending on the space available to display the data. For example, each division on the axis may represent 1, 2, 5, 10 or 100, etc. units.

sequence An ordered set of numbers that follow a rule to give the next term. For example, 3, 9, 27, 81, 243 … is a sequence, as each number is 3 times the number before it.

square number The result of multiplying a number by itself. For example, 5^2 or 5 squared is equal to $5 \times 5 = 25$.

square root The square of a square root of a number gives you the number. The square root of 9 (or $\sqrt{9}$) is 3, because $3 \times 3 = 3^2 = 9$.

stem-and-leaf diagram A method of displaying statistical data. The tens digits of a number will be the 'stem' and the units digits will be the 'leaves'.

subtract (*subtract* is a verb; *subtraction* is the noun) A basic operation of arithmetic, shown by a subtraction (−) sign. Subtraction is the difference between two numbers. For example, $25 - 12 = 13$. (See also *difference*.)

symmetry When one shape is exactly the same as another shape if you turn it over, slip it or slide it (that is, under a transformation), it is said 'to have symmetry'. For example, the letter T has one line of symmetry (a mirror down the middle would produce an identical reflection), the letter N has rotational symmetry of order two (a rotation of 180° would produce an image that looks like an N).

temperature How hot or cold something is, measured in the Celsius or Fahrenheit scale, using a thermometer.

tessellation Identical shapes tessellate. They should have no gaps and should not overlap. Space that is filled this way, is called a tessellation.

triangle A three-sided polygon. The interior angles add up to 180°. Triangles may be classified as:
1. scalene – no sides of the triangle are equal in length (and no angles are equal)
2. equilateral – all the sides of the triangles are equal in length (and all the angles are equal)
3. isosceles – two of the sides of the triangle are equal in length (and two angles are equal)
4. a right-angled triangle has an interior angle equal to 90°.

unlikely An outcome that does not have much chance of happening.

value The result of a calculation. For example, 6×7 gives the value of 42. Or, how much something is worth.

Notes

William Collins' dream of knowledge for all began with the publication of his first book in 1819. A self-educated mill worker, he not only enriched millions of lives, but also founded a flourishing publishing house. Today, staying true to this spirit, Collins books are packed with inspiration, innovation and practical expertise. They place you at the centre of a world of possibility and give you exactly what you need to explore it.

Collins. Freedom to teach.

Published by Collins
An imprint of HarperCollinsPublishers
77–85 Fulham Palace Road
Hammersmith
London
W6 8JB

Browse the complete Collins catalogue at
www.collinseducation.com

10 9 8 7 6 5 4 3 2 1
ISBN-13 978-0-00-734021-7

Chris Pearce asserts his moral rights to be identified as the author of this work

British Library Cataloguing in Publication Data
A Catalogue record for this publication is available from the British Library

Commissioned by Priya Govindan
Project managed by Aimée Walker
Edited and proofread by Brian Asbury and Marian Bond
Answer check by Marian Bond
Cover design by Angela English
Concept design by Nigel Jordan
Illustrations by Kathy Baxendale and Gray Publishing
Design and typesetting by Linda Miles,
Lodestone Publishing
Functional maths and problem-solving pages designed and illustrated by Jerry Fowler and edited and proofread by Rachel Faulkner
Glossary by Gudrun Kaiser
Production by Simon Moore
Printed and bound by L.E.G.O. S.p.A. Italy

Acknowledgements
The publishers have sought permission from Edexcel to reproduce questions from past GCSE Mathematics papers.

The publishers wish to thank the following for permission to reproduce photographs. Every effort has been made to trace copyright holders and to obtain their permission for the use of copyright material. The publishers will gladly receive any information enabling them to rectify any error or omission at the first opportunity.

p.18–19 © Demid/Dreamstime.com; © Dtguy/ Dreamstime.com, © Heysues23/Dreamstime.com, © Andres Rodriguez/Dreamstime.com; p.32–33 © Albo/ Dreamstime.com, © Eddy Van Ryckeghem/Dreamstime.com; p.40–41 © George Tsartsianidis/Dreamstime.com, © Rfoxphoto/Dreamstime.com, © Py2000/Dreamstime.com, © Yory Frenklakh/Dreamstime.com, © Aneta Skoczewska/ Dreamstime.com, © Anthony Baggett/Dreamstime.com, © Pål Sundsøy/Dreamstime.com, © Videowokart/ Dreamstime.com, © Asier Villafranca/Dreamstime.com, © Alexey Federov/Dreamstime.com, © Tatiana Grozetskaya/ Dreamstime.com, © Mihai-bogdan Lazar/Dreamstime.com, © Jorisvo/Dreamstime.com, © Bbbar/Dreamstime.com, © Aleksandrov Valentin Mihaylovich/Dreamstime.com, © Awie Badenhorst/Dreamstime.com, © Young Kimpark/ Dreamstime.com, © David May/Dreamstime.com; pp.56–57 © Jiri Moucka/Dreamstime.com; p.72–73 © Keith Gentry/ Dreamstime.com, © Mrallen/Dreamstime.com, © Steve Liptrot/Dreamstime.com; pp.90–91 © Yenwen Lu/ iStockphoto.com, © Nicky Linzey/Dreamstime.com, © Jyothi/Dreamstime.com; pp.102–103 © Lance Bellers/ Dreamstime.com, © Sburel/Dreamstime.com, © Shaw/ Wikimedia Commons; p.111 © Crown/dft.gov.uk, © Honda UK/hondauk-media.co.uk, © Renault/renault.co.uk; pp114–115 © Woldee/Dreamstime.com, © Chris Pearce; pp.130–131 © Ruslandashinsky/Dreamstime.com; p.140 © Crown/ hse.gov.uk; p.141 © Oliver Kessler/ iStockphoto.com, © Andrew Zarivny/iStockphoto.com; pp.140–141 © Niek/Dreamstime.com, © Astra490/Dreamstime.com, © Clearviewstock/Dreamstime.com, © Jerry Fowler; p.153 © Sir John Tenniel/Wikimedia Commons; pp.156–157 © Olivier Meerson/Dreamstime.com, © Jjayo/Dreamstime.com, © Fedels/Dreamstime.com; p.165 © Roman Peregontsev/ iStockphoto.com, © Sherwin McGehee/iStockphoto.com; pp. 168–169 © Jerry Fowler; p.15 answers © R. A. Nonenmacher/Wikimedia Commons.

With thanks to Jan Parry (Secondary Mathematics Consultant, Leicester), Peter Thompson and Annie Sutton (The Angmering School), and Steve Nutting (Oasis Academy, Shirley Park).